The Legacy
of
Philippe Pinel

WALTHER RIESE, M.D.

Emeritus Associate Professor
of Neurology, Psychiatry and the History of Medicine
at the Medical College of Virginia.
Professor emeritus on the Medical Faculty
of the Johann Wolfgang Goethe University in Frankfurt a. M.
Formerly Chargé de Recherches
du Centre National de la Recherche Scientifique (Paris),
and formerly Consulting Neuropathologist
to the Department of Mental Hygiene and Hospitals
of the Commonwealth of Virginia.

The Legacy of Philippe Pinel

AN INQUIRY INTO THOUGHT ON MENTAL ALIENATION

by

WALTHER RIESE, M.D.

SPRINGER PUBLISHING COMPANY, INC., NEW YORK

This investigation was supported by Public Health Service Research Grant RO/MH 12875 from the U. S. Department of Health, Education, and Welfare Public Health Service, Bethesda, Maryland

Printed in U.S.A.

This book is dedicated to

DR. HERTHA RIESE

TRAITÉ

MÉDICO-PHILOSOPHIQUE

SUR

L'ALIÉNATION MENTALE,

OU

LA MANIE,

PAR PH. PINEL,

Professeur de l'École de Médecine de Paris, Médecin en chef de l'Hospice National des femmes, ci-devant la Salpêtrière, et Membre de plusieurs Sociétés savantes.

Avec Figures représentant des formes de crâne ou des portraits d'Aliénés.

A PARIS,

CHEZ RICHARD, CAILLE ET RAVIER,
Libraires, rue Haute-Feuille, N°. 11.

AN IX.

Title page of the 1801 (AN IX) edition of Pinel's
Traité médico-philosophique sur l'aliénation mentale

ACKNOWLEDGMENTS

All translations from the French not specifically attributed to other sources are the work of the author in collaboration with Mrs. Louise W. Morton.

I wish to acknowledge the indefatigable assistance of my editorial secretary, Mrs. Frances Benedek.

Contents

"Q"

All quotations are indented. Since many quotations are lengthy, extending over several pages, "Q" indicates the indent for the convenience of the reader.

The Legacy
of
Philippe Pinel

I | The Importance of Pinel

"C'est une belle partie de la médecine que l'histoire et le traitement de la folie: des faits bien choisis sur cette matière éclaireroient singulièrement l'étude de l'homme." (Cabanis, Quelques Principes et Quelques Vues sur les Secours Publics, *An XI-1803*) .

Philippe Pinel stands out in the history of civilization and medicine for his courageous and successful endeavor to secure for the mentally ill person acknowledgment as a patient suffering from disease (and not from witchcraft, possession, or sin), requiring medical care (and not punishment), and entitled, above all, to the full status of a human being and a citizen (*citoyen*). The achievements of those great men who challenge all limitations cannot be fully understood unless we conceive of them as expressions and signals of the times and circumstances in which they originated.

Pinel was neither the first nor the last author whose views on disease were rooted in philosophical doctrines, the technical language of which often reappears in the vocabulary of the medical authors adopting the particular doctrine. This is often the source of an esoteric terminology and a cause of misunderstanding among physicians aiming at an intelligible interpretation and sound therapy of that same disease.

But Pinel did not introduce nor borrow a language the meaning of which originated in a single individual's mind. Such "schools of thought" often revealed their secrets only to the initiated and denied entrance to those who did not want to capitulate before testing the new and still unknown ground. What distinguishes Pinel's endeavor from all esoteric beginnings is his intention to reach out for a *theory of medical experience* as a safe ground on which to analyze and treat mental alienation.

Pinel was a son of the eighteenth century, which handed down to him that theory of experience, known as sensationalism, that was linked with the names of Locke and Condillac. In this respect, his thought was indeed condemned to remain tributary to the century which gave birth to his philosophical model. But whatever the truth and the limits of a theory of experience rooted in sensationalism, the eighteenth century was an enlightened one that tried to envision man at his best and at his most universal. Pinel did no more than—in his own terms—to propose the general working of the human mind to those who were eager for sound instruction *("Je ne fais que proposer à l'homme qui est avide d'une instruction solide, la marche générale de l'esprit humain")*. Thus, the early history of psychiatry is rooted in the history of the human intellect, and man in alienation *reaffirms* himself and all the powers and faculties to which he owes his health and his greatness. In passing from mental health to mental alienation, man does not cross a frontier separating forever two entirely different areas of his mental frame; the constituents of this frame are still active and recognizable in alienation (though they are involved in those new and hazardous constructions which we call his symptoms), and can still be interpreted and classified according to the same basic faculties of the mind which are exposed by the analysis of the sane individual.

Pinel's human figure and his liberating achievements (e.g., unchaining the insane) have been traced by others to their purely *humanitarian* sources. Though the author is far from underestimating the humanitarian aspect of Pinel's work, he intends first of all to bring the eminent alienist into focus with regard to the intellectual and moral spirit of his time, to his medical philosophy shaped by the great thought currents of the eighteenth century and, above all, by the basic principles of Hippocratic medicine.

There is a strong *observational* element in Hippocratic medicine, though it is by no means its only constituent. With Greek medicine, about 2,500 years ago, the study and careful examination of the sick came into being. Time and again, the tradition was lost in the march of time and in the course of medical history; speculation, dogma, and so-called medical systems were substituted for observation. Pinel was a fervent adherent to undogmatic observation and to Hippocratic medicine.

While there is ample evidence of Pinel's kind and gentle nature (detectable, above all, in his *traitement moral*), on these grounds alone a courageous, planned, well-founded, and organized work could hardly be brought to its end and perfection. I have attempted to present, for what I believe is the first time, Pinel's approach to the mentally ill as a logical result of his Hippocratic view of disease as an historical chapter in an individual's life. In a brief but remarkable introductory historical sketch preceding his treatise on mental alienation, Pinel himself traced the birth, decline, rebirth, and different versions of this view of disease. Trained by the humanities, his mind was that of a scholar rather than that of a sentimental apologist. Nor was his love for his fellow human beings merely a spontaneous manifestation of nature; it, too, was sponsored and shaped by the teaching of the philosophers of the eighteenth century, and above all by his friend Condorcet. Adapted from contemporary philosophers, Pinel's method was an analytic and experimental rather than an intuitive or visionary one.

The Meaning of the Term, "The Legacy of Pinel"

The *legacy of Pinel* is understood by me to be implied in his major work which bears the title *Traité médico-philosophique sur l'aliénation mentale*. To reach the genuine meaning of the qualification *médico-philosophique*, I found it necessary to consult the *Dictionnaire de l'Académie Française*, whose fourth edition was published in 1762, i.e., in Pinel's lifetime. Pinel was born in 1745; in 1762 he entered the seminary of the *pères de la doctrine chrétienne* in Lavaur (28). The dictionary of the French Academy defines a philosopher as a person who devotes himself to the study of science and who tries to derive effects from their causes and their principles (*connaître les effets par leurs causes et par leurs principes*). There is anticipated in this definition the whole program of Pinel's endeavor and his main thesis, namely, to derive the causes of insanity from the passions.

In still more general terms, his legacy is understood to represent the philosophical and medical treasure which he inherited from his intellectual ancestors and which he in turn left to the succeeding generations.

II

The Status of Psychiatry at the Time of Pinel

Description of a Public Insane Asylum in the Days When Pinel Received His First Appointment to the Charge of Bicêtre, Given by Pariset in his "Eloge de Pinel" (34)

"Q" Vice, crime, misfortune, infirmity, diseases, the most varied and the most revolting, all were heaped together and treated alike. The buildings were untenable. Men crouched, covered with filth, in cells of stone that were narrow, cold, dripping, without air or light, and furnished only with a litter of straw, rarely renewed and soon infected—hideous lairs in which one would have hesitated to shut up the vilest animal. The insane, thrown into these sewers, were at the mercy of their keepers and their keepers were malefactors from the prisons. The wretched patients were loaded with chains and tied with ropes like convicts. Handed over thus to the cruelty of their guardians, they were made the butt of insulting raillery or of blind and wanton brutality. The injustice of their savage treatment transported them with rage; and despair and wrath inflaming their deranged minds, drew from them night and day cries and howlings that rendered still more dreadful the clanking of their chains. Some, more patient or more cunning, showed themselves insensible to such outrages; but they only concealed their frenzy to gratify it more surely. They watched with their eyes the movements of their tormentors until, surprising them in a helpless attitude, they struck them with blows of their chains on the head or stomach and dashed them dying at their feet. Thus, ferocity on one side and murder on the other.

4

Pinel's Own Account

"Q" Nothing has contributed more to the rapid improvement of modern natural history than the spirit of minute and accurate observation. The habit of analytical investigation, thus adopted, has induced an accuracy of expression and a propriety of classification which have themselves in no small degree contributed to the advancement of natural knowledge. Convinced of the essential importance of using the same means in the illustration of a subject so new and so difficult as that of the present work, it will be seen that I have availed myself of its application in all or most of the instances of this most calamitous disease that occurred during my practice at the Asylum de Bicêtre.

On entering upon my duties at that hospital, everything presented to me the appearance of chaos and confusion. Some of my unfortunate patients labored under the horrors of a most gloomy and desponding melancholy. Others were furious, and subject to the influence of a perpetual delirium. Some appeared to possess a correct judgment upon most subjects, but were occasionally agitated by violent sallies of maniacal fury, while those of another class were sunk into a state of stupid idiotism and imbecility. Symptoms so different, and all comprehended under the general title of insanity, required, on my part, much study and discrimination; and to secure order in the establishment and success to the practice, I determined upon adopting such a variety of measures, both as discipline and treatment, as my patients required, and my limited opportunity permitted. . . .

. . . I first of all took a general statement of the symptoms of my patients. To ascertain their characteristic peculiarities, the survey was followed by cautious and repeated examinations into the condition of individuals. All our new cases were entered at great length upon the journals of the house. Due attention was paid to the changes of the seasons and the weather, and their respective influences upon the patients were minutely noticed. Having a peculiar attachment for the more general method of descriptive history, I did not confine myself to any exclusive mode of arranging my observations, nor to any one system of nosography. The facts which I have thus collected are now admitted to the consideration of the public, in the form of a regular treatise. . . .

"Q" . . . Public asylums for maniacs have been regarded as places of confinement for such of its members as have become dangerous to the peace of society. The managers of those institutions, who are frequently men of little knowledge and less humanity, have been permitted to exercise toward their innocent prisoners a most arbitrary system of cruelty and violence, while experience affords ample and daily proofs of the happier effects of a mild, conciliating treatment, rendered effective by steady and dispassionate firmness (4).

Pinel's Own Report on His Reform

The habit of keeping maniacs uninterruptedly chained is an admirable invention indeed if one aims at perpetuating their rage for the duration of their confinement, if one wants to make up for the lack of zeal of an ignorant supervisor, to keep burning in the hearts of the patients a steady exasperation and a concentrated desire for revenge, and if one wants to arouse tumult and disturbance in the hospitals. Those inconveniences aroused my concerned attention during the first years of the Revolution, at the time when I was a doctor at Bicêtre hospital, and I utterly regret not having been able to see the happy end of such a barbarous and routine custom. On the other hand, I gained a certain peace of mind by knowing that I could rely on the skill of the supervisor (i.e., M. Pussin) of that hospital, who wished, no less ardently than myself, to put an end to such a forgetfulness of the right principles. Fortunately, he succeeded two years later (4 Prairial, An VI), and no measure was ever better planned or followed by greater success. Forty unfortunate, insane patients who had groaned under the weight of their chains for a greater or lesser number of years were freed, in spite of the fears expressed by the Central Office. They were permitted to walk freely in the yard, their arms only being restrained in a straitjacket; during the night, they were turned loose in their cells. It must be noted that, by so doing, a stop was put to the unhappy accidents of which the orderlies were often the victims, as they had often been unexpectedly hit or contused by the insane, chained, and constantly infuriated patients. One of these patients had been fettered for thirty-six years, another for forty-five. Both had, nevertheless, preserved their freedom of

"Q" motion and they walked slowly inside the hospital. Memory has been preserved of one of these patients who had been chained for eighteen years in a dark cell; when he first saw the sun again, in all its glory, he exclaimed in a kind of ecstasy, "How long it has been since I have seen such a wonderful thing!" (61, p. 1228).

III | Definitions and Demarcations

Notes on the Term "Mental Disease"

The ambiguous meaning of the terms "mental" or "psychical" has been responsible for more than one dialectic arising from the very concept and name of mental disease and extending throughout the entire history of psychiatry. The dialectic culminates in the polemic of those believing in insanity as a *somatic* disorder against those deriving it from *psychological* sources. It is an ever-renewed and never-ending controversy. That it reached the proportions of that famous struggle between the two schools of thought in German psychiatry about a century ago was no more than an incidental outgrowth of the basic dialectic. The latter can only be silenced by disclosing the equivocal use made by both parties involved of the terms "mental" or "psychical."

Though it is true that the mentally ill person has *experiences* of his own, it remains equally true that he can have them only because he is still in full possession of those functions, intuitive and intellectual, which enable him to build up a coherent world of objects, to situate them in space and time, and to establish dynamic relations between them. True, his spatial and chronological experiences, as well as the relations established, are very *specific* and incommensurable with ours. Here are the sources of that attitude which considers the mentally ill as far removed from ourselves and beyond the reach of our own experience and understanding. But in so far as space, time, and relating thought remain instrumental in building up any experience, even the strangest one, these functions are the same in the mentally ill person as in us, to that extent we live in a common world with him. Even should these functions be given the qualification of "psychical," they are, nevertheless, universal. Empty in themselves, they are far from becoming subject to disease which remains a whole of specific relations holding together specific data perceptible in a concrete space and time.

We have reason to believe that our bodies and particularly, though not exclusively, our brains, play important roles in the building up of concrete and individual experiences, and to that extent mental disease (as well as mental health) has its physical aspect. But it also remains true that the mentally ill make and communicate their experiences in their proper (namely, psychical) terms, which do not betray the physical ground from which they spring or with which they are associated. In fact, no immediate experience teaches us which cerebral or glandular activities are involved when we are in the states of love, hatred, or anger; these we know only at their psychical face value. Nor are we in possession of the knowledge of the interrelation between the physical and the psychical. To reach the psychical through the physical remains, therefore, an adventure whose outcome cannot be predicted. At least psychotherapy, though also unpredictable as to its success, can claim this superiority over physical treatment, that it meets the patient's questions, sufferings, and needs in their proper and immediate terms.

The End of an Argument: One Method of Thought Against Another

As soon as the physician addresses the individual, he passes from the physiological concept of disease to a psychological one; thus from one method of thought to another. This passage reflects the same change in method which we adopt when we communicate with our fellow human beings, trying to understand, in order to explain, their behavior as individuals. Their specific physiologic processes, mostly unknown, do not enter that chain of thoughts which we trust will lead to the present behavior as its final link. Since in human behavior that final link is understood to be a psychic one, no physiological link would be of explanatory assistance; through its basically different structure it remains entirely unrelated to the chain of psychic events, their specific nature and direction.

The individual, mentally disturbed or not, has and communicates his experiences in their proper (namely, psychical) terms, which do not betray the physical ground from which they spring or with which they are associated. In fact, as we have said before, he is not conscious of the physiological activities which are involved when he is in the state of love, hate or anger.

But do we not admit the psychic effects of purely physical, above all, traumatic happenings? In fact, surreptitiously, we translate the simple fact of the disturbed physical integrity into the language of psychic processes. We demonstrate, or at least we postulate, that the trauma was associated with psychic effects which added up to the whole of processes leading to the final result, i.e., a nervous or mental symptom or disease. Thus, we endow these effects with specific directions admitting of their integration into the history of neurosis or psychosis. Should we lack sufficient factual evidence supporting this causal analysis, and should we nevertheless remain convinced of the specific pathogenic influence of trauma on an individual's thought and action, we fall back to more general assumptions, such as "lowered resistance." But it is obvious that the explanatory value of such assumptions cannot compete with the objective proof of actual psychic effects which we are able to coordinate with the general line of development embodied in the history of neurosis or psychosis. It is not intelligible that purely physical or traumatic procedures should have therapeutic effects in psychic disorders unless these procedures are thought to be succeeded, or are actually succeeded, by psychic ones apt to release or reinforce the stream of thoughts and emotions flowing towards an as yet unknown future which, we trust, will bring improvement, if not cure, to the patient. Thus, in the final analysis, we do not allow the individual, conceived as a center and source of specific experiences, to become consciously indebted to his physiologic equipment. Again, as soon as we leave the sphere of an anonymous life to enter that of an individual and his inner experiences, as in psychotherapy or in interhuman relations at large, we give up the physiological approach. The history of the human soul is written in its own terms.

The analysis made here of the two methods of thought involved, and its use for overcoming the difficulties implied in the opposition of the physical and psychical, is very different from certain contemporary tendencies which try to escape the intellectual emergency arising from this opposition simply by postulating the famous unit of soul and body and by promptly treating the patient through both physical and psychical means at the same time. I understand that the psychotherapist meets the patient on purely psychical grounds and does not allow prescriptions to enter the planning and inner organization of his psychical approach; nor is the patient, as soon as he is drawn into the orbit of educational and diplomatic influences and given responsibilities, allowed to retreat behind the presumable or actual effects of drugs. It is true, of course, that the patient is a unit of soul and body, a statement conveying no great substantial knowledge as long as we have no precise idea of the nature of this unit—an idea we will probably never reach. It has been said that "physical" and "psychical" are but two aspects of the same organism. This statement, however, does not eliminate the difference between the two "aspects." The spatial character which distinguishes physical and physiological manifestations is denied to psychical ones. After all, the patients themselves experience the difference unmistakably. Neither does the assumption of an identity lying behind the two different aspects eliminate the difference in method of thought with which we approach each of them. Nor does the assumption imply the conclusion that by addressing one of the two aspects we necessarily reach both of them. The unit I have in mind, and to which one turns in psychotherapeutical dialogue is, to use Benjamin Rush's term, the unit of "the human figure." This is understood to be the history of a man's emotions, their effects on his decisions (past and present), interhuman relations, shortcomings, and successes—in brief, the history and structure of the personality as it emerges as the result of the physician's own integrating thought.

To stress it once again: the physician passing from the physical genesis of mental *disease* or behavior to action aimed at the diseased *individual*, truly passes from one method of thought to another; in fact, he passes from one concept of disease to another. The search for the sources of mental disease implies etiologic and anatomical concepts. These do not promise a view of disease as a coherent whole, subject to the laws of time and revealing order and direction. In fact, whenever the physician tries to obtain this coherent view, he turns to historical, biographical, and psychological concepts. For the time being, he can leave undecided, or regard as irrelevant, which etiologic factors, pathogenic mechanisms, or regional structures may be responsible for a condition whose inner content and coherence alone are at stake in his embracing view.

In brief, the physician turning to physical agents to bring about a change in the mental condition of his patient simply relinquishes the view of disease as a coherent whole, subject to the intrinsic rules of mental life. He adopts the etiologic concept and thinks in terms of physio-pathologic mechanisms rather than in terms of biography. Drugs, shocks, or psychosurgical interventions cannot be included in the chain of intelligible links holding together that evolutionary history which we call mental disease. It is the crudeness of matter and physical agents at large, foreign to animated life and human conscience, which makes these agents unfit substitutes for truly biographical events whose continuity they rather disrupt. We conceive them only as instrumental in promoting or facilitating mental experiences which, we trust, will emerge after the administration of physical agents to become constituents of the biography and determine a happier course. Thus, we relinquish the etiologic concept in its turn and subreptitiously reconstitute the inner structure of the disease as the coherent whole of inner experiences; we pass from one method of thought to another.

To conclude, we do not give up the distinction between the physical and the psychical; nor do we simply and dogmatically postulate their unit. Instead, we disclose the alternative use which human intelligence perpetually makes, according to needs, of two methods of thought, each of them embodying a different concept of disease.

Thus comes to an end the famous controversy between those believing in somatic sources of mental disease and those believing in psychogenesis. The "somatic," conceived as a regional lesion, trauma, drug, or surgical intervention, all of them equally foreign to the nature and history of the inner experiences of the patient, cannot be made truly active constituents of the history of life and disease. Only by bringing their immediate effects, crude and unrelated as they are in themselves, into inner relation with the whole history and evolution of the individual, can we hope to influence the course of inner experiences by physical means. But then we fall back upon psychotherapy, and the physician bringing the crude effects of brain lesions, natural or artificial, in line with the patient's biography, is indeed practicing psychotherapy in organic conditions.

It is true that Philippe Pinel referred to "an interruption of the chain of delirious ideas induced by the suddenness of the shock" (i.e., the "bath of surprise"), and to "the general agitation of the system experienced from this process." It is equally true that on the same occasion (4, pp. 261, 264, 265), he referred to "the enthusiast Johannes van Helmont, who has made some valuable remarks upon the durable effects of sudden immersion in cold water in some cases of mental derangement" (Pinel asserting indeed, that this method, however successful in some instances, might in others be extremely dangerous). Pinel did not undertake an epistemologic analysis of the experiences. But I submit that the author of a medico-*philosophic* treatise on insanity and the inaugurator of *moral* treatment must have passed surreptitiously from one mode of thinking (in *physical* terms) to another mode of thinking (in *psychic* terms). The latter then stands indeed on equal terms with delirious ideas whose chain may be thought of as being interrupted by the shock (41, pp. 75-137).

The Perpetual Danger of Supernatural Diagnosis

Though it seemed that the author of the Hippocratic treatise, *On the Sacred Disease,* eliminated forever any exceptional nature and etiology of insanity, thus establishing natural diagnosis on the firm ground of sound and independent reasoning, the latter did not obtain a lasting victory. Not only did supernatural etiology continue to live side by side with the natural one in antiquity; it rose again to an unheard-of power in the middle ages and the Renaissance. In fact, it never ceased to invade human thought, though at times only on an infinitesimal scale in civilized communities. Why have most educated people, laymen and physicians, time and again been tempted and willing to trace insanity back to moral and religious sources? The reason for this most impressive, alarming, and ever-recurrent attitude becomes obvious as soon as we take the experiences of the mentally ill for what they are, not denying them their reality but rather trying to test their structure in the light of man's experiences at large, regardless of the conditions and circumstances in which they arise; in brief, if we re-experience them in their fullness and significance. Then we may identify them with some of man's basic experiences and inner attitudes. It still remains to be shown that the mentally ill's feelings of sin, guilt, and repentance, their terrifying expectation and imagination of imminent punishment (and also their confidence in redemption), their idea of the far-reaching impact of their own thought and action on their fellow-men and man's destiny as a whole, are experiences basically different in their living states from ours. Truly, the inner experiences of guilt and repentance do not convey in themselves the criteria of health and disease.

Should we then give up this distinction, should we ignore or refuse the legacy of Pinel and once again turn over the mentally ill person to religious authorities instead of admitting him to the doctor's office or the ward of an institution? There remains one distinction between the two conditions. It is not to be sought in the quality of the contents considered—in other words, it is not a phenomenological one. It can only be sought in the relation of the experienced state to the individual's history and growth. If the religious experiences are the result of an inner evolution whose end (rather than its beginning) they would mark; if they emerge as the final link of a chain of conscious steps, all converging towards them, if the biography implies their anticipation; in brief, if the religious experiences are in an organic and intelligible union with life and personality, we should be most reluctant to make the statement of disease. Though in religious experience man feels tied to inner forces and yields to commands he recognizes as inescapable powers, there is no room for supernatural *diagnosis*. We turn to the latter in those instances in which an individual is overwhelmed by foreign and unforeseen experiences that, far from springing from the individual's history, specific needs, and the search for truth, are forced upon him. There remain those rare cases in which the sudden invasion of consciousness is instrumental in releasing, for the first time, a genuine religious experience. *This is revelation.* One might argue that at the time it occurs, supernatural diagnosis is legitimate. It remains true, however, that revelation entails a sequence of inner events which are coherent, intelligible, and, above all, deeply anchored in the person's life, structure, and conduct.

Demoniacal Possession

Were we to be satisfied with a simple enumeration of the various steps and stages leading Pinel to his final view on mental alienation and his moral treatment, his legacy would neither be evaluated nor saved in its full scope. It is for this reason alone that I feel justified, if not bound, to reopen, though briefly, the whole problem of demoniacal possession, which indeed has been treated in the past and present by more than one competent author. Moreover, I feel strengthened in my decision to give some space to the history and inner structure of demoniacal possession by the fact that new interpretations make use of the newly gained insights into the inner experiences of human existences living under threat and terror. I realize that the limit set by clinical psychiatry might thereby be transgressed. A third reason for the relatively small opening I am giving to the problem of demoniacal possession lies in the fact that new interpretations fit perfectly with Pinel's major thesis of the human passions as the ultimate sources of mental alienation.

The following passage from Pinel's *Treatise on Insanity* is a clear example of his views on demoniacal possession:

"Q" The credit attached to the impostures of demoniacal possession in the writings of Wierus are not to be wondered at, when we consider that his works were published towards the middle of the seventeenth century, and bear as much reference to theology as to medicine. This author, whose errors admit of some palliation in consideration of the influence of popular prejudices, appears to have been a great adept in the mysteries of exorcism. He records, with great solicitude, the gifts of demoniacal prediction, the perfidious and malicious tricks of the devil under the human figure, and the forms of celebrated characters which in different places he assumed to show himself upon the earth. "When a man," says the judicious Dr. Mead, "rends his clothes and walks naked, strikes all who come in his way with terror, inflicts severe wounds on his own person; when he is so furious as to burst the strongest chains; when he haunts the most gloomy solitudes, or wanders among the tombs and cries out that he is possessed by the devil, there can be no difficulty in ascertaining the nature of his disorder." Can we suppose the demoniacs, whose histories are recorded in theological writings, to be any more than extravagant maniacs? We need only visit a lunatic asylum in order to appreciate justly the nature of their pretended inspiration. In a word, demoniacs of all descriptions are to be classed either with maniacs or melancholics. What more calculated to excite in weak minds such chimerical fancies than mania without delirium, conjoined to and chiefly consisting in a propensity to acts of maniacal extravagance? To punish the misconduct, however extravagant, of a man who avows his inability to govern his own actions, would be cruel: attempts to rectify errors, the absurdity of which he is ready to acknowledge and lament, would be attended with little advantage. Strong antispasmodics, the charms of music, or the excitement of profound emotion, are the only remedies adapted to effect any durable change. Such are the means which priests of all ages have adopted with equal avidity and address. Such, among others, were those which were practiced annually at Besançon, during the celebration of the feast of Saint Suaire, famed for the great number of madmen, or demoniacs as they were called, who

"Q" resorted thither to be cured. In the presence of an immense crowd of spectators, who were elevated on a spacious amphitheatre, the pretended demoniacs were brought forth, guarded by soldiers, and agitated by all the movements and distortions characteristic of raving madness. The priests, in their official habiliments, proceeded, with great gravity, to their exorcisms. From a distant part of the church, and concealed from view, were heard melodious notes of martial music. Upon a certain signal, a flag stained with blood, with the name of Saint Suaire inscribed upon it, was brought out three different times, and hoisted amidst the acclamations of the astonished multitude and the roaring of cannon from the citadel. Upon the minds of the credulous spectators a solemn impression was thus produced, and they cried out, with the utmost excess of enthusiasm, *"Miracle! Miracle!"* This pompous spectacle was exhibited once a year by the priests, to show their power over demonomania. There were some maniacs who were actually cured by the impression produced by these rituals of fantastic solemnity. Enlightened medicine knows how to appreciate religious ceremonies of this description, at the same time that it admires the address of priests of all ages in conciliating the respect, and in making impressions upon the minds of the laity (4, pp. 237-239).

A major part of medieval psychiatry seems indeed to be written in terms of *demoniacal possession*. Ever since psychiatry was shaped by observational and experimental medicine, and medicine itself by natural science, there has been no doubt in any modern physician's mind that demoniacal possession was a symptom of mental alienation. The tortures once inflicted on allegedly or avowedly possessed individuals are generally considered to be a crime against humanity, and those fifteenth- and sixteenth-century physicians who denounced this crime and claimed for the unfortunate victims medical treatment instead of punishment and torture, are considered and honored as forerunners of Pinel and modern psychiatry. On the other hand, one could always find those who denied the thesis according to which all cases of demoniacal possession would have to be considered cases of insanity. The church itself has always been cautious in the matter; in cases of doubt or perplexity it turned to medical experts before reaching a decision.

Among the mental states reported in medieval literature, theological and secular, the following ones must arouse the suspicion of the alienist: convulsive disorders; hallucinatory scenes and meetings with the Devil, demons, and other attendants known or unknown to the possessed individual (who sometimes gave the most detailed description of the Devil appearing under the most various guises and shapes) ; the Devil's obscene offers and attacks, to which the possessed person perhaps submitted with delight; alleged transportation through the air to often far-distant meeting places, and retransportation by the same means to the home of the possessed person, known, however, to have remained in his bed during the whole night of the diabolic adventure; anaesthesia, total or partial; and sudden and most violent aggressive impulses, suicidal or homicidal, often directed against the most cherished persons—relatives, husband, wife, and even one's own small children.

It seems that, after all, the history of demoniacal possession cannot be considered a closed chapter of human and medical thought. In the eyes of T. K. Oesterreich, the documents collected by him in a monumental volume, (33) ". . . have placed beyond doubt the wide distribution of the phenomena of possession over the habitable globe." In another recent publication (30) , a most eminent contemporary neurologist whose name is linked with more than one discovery in the field of clinical neurology and neuropathology, the late professor at the Medical Faculty of Paris. J. Lhermitte, wished to demarcate sharply the competence of the physician from that of the theologian or exorcist who may enter the scene after the physician has dismissed the case as a non-medical problem.

In all good faith, Lhermitte strove for safe differential diagnostic criteria admitting of a distinction between true diabolic possession and demoniacal pseudo-possession; apparently he did not realize that the sixteenth-century physician, F. Plater, preceded him in this undertaking. Lhermitte thought that a morbid process was likely to be the etiologic factor in those cases in which the so-called demoniacal possession offered to the medical observer all of the characteristics of a genuine paranoid state, and in which it followed the laws of the latter and yielded to the same therapy. In contrast, he said, one should turn to the qualified theologian in those cases in which the signs of possession appeared only as "parasitic" phenomena or as associated with the highest qualities of spirit and heart. The author left the question unanswered whether or not the demon may reveal its presence exclusively by mental or physical disease which may even prove to be accessible to scientific treatment.

The medieval theologians, philosophers, and physicians believed indeed that an evil spirit could produce cerebral lesions succeeded by hallucinations, convulsions or suicide, at times in an epidemic fashion, due to a massive invasion of an entire country by groups of demons (14, I, 117-118).

Among the enlightened sixteenth-century physicians who tried to save many a so-called possessed individual and witch from the stake and to prove their mental alienation, frequent malingery, and unconscious lies, Weyer* (6) has gained the greatest fame. But he still believed in spirits and devils. With greater interest (14) we learn that in the sixteenth century suicides were frequent among mentally disturbed individuals who often ingested fragments of bone, feathers and iron; convulsions associated with delusions were frequent among nuns and in boys' schools, and they often reached epidemic proportions.

Felix Plater (1536-1614), another great physician and alienist of the same period, also believed in evil spirits as etiologic factors of mental disorders. For the first time we encounter an attempt to establish *differential-diagnostic* criteria allowing of a distinction between demoniacal possession on the one hand and mania and melancholia on the other. Though the symptomatology is about the same in both conditions, a demoniacal etiology exists, according to Plater, in those cases in which the afflicted individual sees spirits around him, remains speechless for a more or less long interval, takes no food, assumes unusual postures, hears the demon speak through his own mouth, is able to predict the future, to divine the presence of hidden objects, and to speak languages which he had neither spoken nor understood prior to his illness.

At this stage of the discussion of our subject, an account, though brief indeed, of Plater's *classification* of mental disorders cannot be avoided. It seems that, from the first awakening of an unprejudiced but still timid study of mental disorders, the latter have been linked with an attempt to classify them; evidently, in no branch of clinical medicine has the need for orientation, system, and order been felt with greater strength than in the doctrine of mental diseases extending from ancient authors to Plater, Pinel, and finally to contemporary psychiatrists.

---

*Johan Weyer (Wierus) was born in 1515 in Grave, North Brabant. He studied in Bonn, Paris, and Orleans. In 1545 he was appointed physician to the municipality of Arnheim. From 1550 to 1578 he was body physician of the duke Wilhelm von Jülich Cleve-Berg. He died in 1588. (Biographical note by E. Ackerknecht)

Plater's Classification of Mental Disorders*

Felix Plater divided mental disorders into the following classes:

I. *De Mentis Imbecilitate:*

Imbecility indicates a person who has a diminution of power of understanding, mental ability, judgment, reason, or memory as compared with the normal man; it may occur in cases of bodily disease, but also in persons quite sound. Four subgroups were distinguished. Among the causes listed was also 'deep wound in the region of the orbit. A man learned in Latin and Greek after recovering from a wound in this position had to begin again to learn the alphabet.' This seems to be the first case of aphasia ever observed; it resulted from brain injury.

We also read that too much study, or too little use of the mind may result in 'imbecility.'

II. *De Mentis Consternatione:*

This is when the senses are to some extent blunted or almost entirely abolished, or the individuals affect sleep unnaturally, or are stupefied. This may be accompanied by sluggishness of body or complete relaxation, with agitation or convulsion or rigidity of body. Ten subdivisions were distinguished, one of them being *Sopor demoniacus:* The persons thus affected 'think they are carried through the air, live pleasantly, lead dances, and associate with demons, and when awake these ideas persist.'

III. *De Mente Alienatione:*

Among the subgroups there were listed *Mania, Melancholia,* but also *Amor.*

IV. *Mentis Defatigatio:*

This is when the internal senses are kept at work to a greater extent or for a longer period than is suitable. *Vigilia* and *Insomnia* were listed as subdivisions, the cause of both being the act of God or that of a demon. ('The cunning of a demon can be got rid of by prayer, by fasting, by amending the mode of life, and by perfect faith.')

*Plater, *Praxis Med.*, 1625.

Plater was not the first medical writer who tried to establish classifications of mental disorders. Similar attempts can be traced back to antiquity (67). The terms most frequently encountered in ancient writers and those of the early centuries of our era are phrenitis, epilepsy, mania, and melancholia, the latter being considered by Aretaeus (died in 138 A. D.) as the *beginning and even part of the disorder called mania*. Other groups established were lethargus and lycanthropy. Avicenna (980-1036) added Amentia or fatuity, delirium, defect of memory, defect of imagination, the insane form of love, incubus, and effeminacy or "pathic" disorder, most of these conditions appearing ill-defined to a modern reader, all of them difficult to identify with the divisions of our present-day classifications. Often the early writers used the presence or absence of fever as a differential diagnostic criterion. Attempts to correlate mental disorders with the brain and the meninges appeared very early in medical history. But as a rule, the humors, their excesses or deficiencies, were called forth to explain mental disorders and to treat them on humoralpathological grounds. The history of the term and concept of catalepsy (55) reflects the history of psychiatric ideas and doctrines of many centuries.

The Fourfold Significance of the Hippocratic Treatise, "On the Sacred Disease"

To the Hippocratic book, *On The Sacred Disease*, a prominent place must be assigned in the history of ideas in psychiatry. Above all, the book marked the passage from religious to rational medicine or, more specifically, *from supernatural to natural diagnosis*. The author definitely rejected the divine character of the disease. The sentence, "Men regard its nature and cause as divine from ignorance, and wonder because it is not at all like to other diseases," conveys two significant ideas. In its first part, the religious or divine etiology is seen to be derived from ignorance. Thus, the passage to rational medicine or natural diagnosis implies the passage to *knowledge*, which emerges as the true criterion and legitimate credential of scientific medicine. The qualification that "this notion of its divinity is kept up by the inability to comprehend it," implies the conclusion that knowledge starts with the ability to comprehend. The text of the book and the method applied by its author leave no doubt that comprehension is believed to be attained as soon as the disease is traced back to its natural cause. This step obviously implied greater difficulties in treatment. "The simplicity of the mode by which it is cured," namely, by purifications and incantations, came to its end. In other words, the passage to natural diagnosis and natural therapy promised no comfort, and the physician, by reaching the greatness of *human* labor, shared at the same time its misery. The idea expressed in the second part of the sentence quoted, ". . . because it is not at all like to other diseases," is elaborated and varied in the text, and repeatedly brought to the reader's attention and insight. ". . . this disease . . . has its nature such as other diseases have." It was the author's intention to *deny to the disease any exceptional nature,* precisely by depriving it of its supernatural etiology. Evidently, it was neither in the author's mind nor in his power to reshape the manifestations or the symptomatology of the disease; his endeavor was strictly limited to the causal interpretation of it. Here he was entirely free, whereas the factual evidence or the perceptible criteria of the disease admitted of no interference. In other words, the clinical picture remained the same, though the interpretation of its origin was submitted to a basic change. *For the first time in the history of medical thought the symptomatology was conceived as admitting different and conflicting causal interpretations.* But the precious idea was lost in post-Hippocratic and medieval medicine. More than 2,000 years after the teaching of the Greek, diseases were still believed to reveal unmistakably just one cause, namely, the supernatural or demoniacal cause.

Finally, the treatise was of greatest significance because it stressed the *physical sources* of insanity, with the *brain* emerging as the regional structure responsible for "madness." Thus took shape, it seems, the neuroanatomical and neuropathological concepts of psychosis. The brain, however, was not understood as yet to be the primary seat of alienation, but was considered to be only secondarily affected. The humors were believed to be the true pathogenic agents. "As long as the brain is at rest, the man enjoys his reason, but the depravement of the brain arises from phlegm and bile. . . ." The whole treatise closes with the following sentence: ". . . whoever is acquainted with such a change in men and can render a man humid and dry, hot and cold by regimen, could also cure this disease if he recognized the proper season for administering his remedies without minding purifications, spells, and all other illiberal practices of a like kind." Thus, mental pathology still remained humoral pathology, and not until the nineteenth century did it lose this character when, under the growing influence of neuroanatomy and neuropathology, the humors were finally dismissed and the solid structures, including the brain, were given the rank of primary movers in mental disease. In fact, it was the *physiological concept* of insanity rather than the anatomical one which was anticipated by the author of *On The Sacred Disease,* and it is because the treatise fits perfectly into the inner coherence and unity of the entire doctrine that one should assign to it the rank of a genuine Hippocratic writing.

IV

The General Idea of Pinel's Endeavor – the "Traite Médico-Philosophique sur l'Aliénation Mentale"

The book by Pinel which proved to have a lasting effect on the final structure of psychiatry bears the title: *Traité médico-philosophique sur l'aliénation mentale* (Paris, 1801). But the philosophical foundation on which the treatise rests is different from that of his *Nosographie philosophique ou la méthode de l'analyse appliquée à la médecine* (Paris, 1798), which was the first of the treatises to embody the views and experiences of the eminent French alienist in clinical medicine at large. It is of the greatest historical and biographical interest to trace the development of Pinel's philosophical ideas and to note the shift which his philosophical *confessions* and *equipment* underwent from his earlier work to his treatise on mental alienation.

Though Pinel's thought was observational rather than conceptual, though he was striving for factual evidence rather than definitions and medical doctrines *(esprit de système)* in his nosography, he could not prevent himself from making statements of a most general character concerning diseases and medicine. Defining his purpose in a negative sense, he wanted to eliminate all that vague and superficial knowledge which he believed to be significant of humoral medicine (2, p. I). Disease, he said, should neither be considered as an incessantly changing picture nor as an incoherent assemblage of reappearing affections which one should fight constantly by remedies, but rather as an indivisible whole from its onset to its end, as a logical entity of characteristic symptoms and a sequence of periods associated with nature's tendencies, most frequently favorable though at times disastrous.

Eternal tribute, Pinel said, should be paid to the observational spirit of Hippocrates, who traced the histories of diseases with as much faithfulness as brevity and profoundness; for twenty centuries he has opened the true path of observation as well as of descriptive medicine. As though he wanted to defend us against a superstitious admiration for his writings, he conveyed in them the means by which to rectify them should they be incorrect, and to extend knowledge still left incomplete by him. Should we not admire, Pinel asked, the analytical method adopted by the father of medicine as the only true and invariable one in the search for truth? Should we not admire his profound wisdom in indicating, by a historical exposition of the facts, the course of nature when left to herself in acute diseases? Should we not admire his striving for broader views on the medical constitution of the seasons, his final generalizations and aphoristic sentences, at times certainly open to exceptions, but always rich in great truths and most often confirmed by enlightened observation? Is not all solid progress made by medicine at all times due to the analytical method, and what may we still expect of its application to the whole doctrine and the public instruction of this science? (2, pp. VII-IX).

What did he understand by his analytical method? Here he cited Locke and he almost copied Locke's French pupil Condillac, whose writings were almost a bible to the spiritual fathers and philosophical sponsors of the French Revolution. To analyze, Condillac said, is nothing more than to observe the qualities of an object in a successive order so as to secure to them their simultaneous order in the mind. But what is this order? Nature herself indicates it; it is the order in which she offers the objects. Some of them attract our attention more particularly; there are the more striking and the more dominant ones, all the others apparently being centered around them. When applied to medicine, the analytical method proceeds by the following steps: at first, one collects several facts of the same kind; then one discards all the variations due to age, constitution, and climate, thus reaching the true concept of a species, simple or complex. Symptoms common to several species constitute by their combination a complex and abstract idea, i.e., that of a genus. The criteria of orders result from the symptoms proper to the different genera and those of classes from the affinities existing between several orders.

The application of the analytical method to medicine was intended by Pinel to secure a faithful history of symptoms and to prevent confusion of one disease with another; in other words, it was intended to serve differential diagnosis. At first, there is exploration of symptoms, regardless of any preconceived hypothesis and solely on the ground of sense impressions. This is followed by a careful study of the patient's premorbid condition, his actual physical and psychical state (at times unobtainable, due to fabrication or deliberate reticence). By way of abstraction, individual variations will be discarded and attention will focus on the specific characters of the disease known by personal observation or by reading other authors. Sagacity is needed to discern different orders of symptoms which when combined form one complicated disease, and when considered separately must be referred to different diseases. At the next stage of this mental procedure, the species and name of the disease will have to be determined, as well as its place in the classificatory scheme. To be on safe grounds, further observation may be needed, and in obscure cases conclusions remain cautious and tentative. The last step consists of the consideration of age, sex, mode of living, and habits likely to influence and to modify the course of the disease. Thus Pinel outlined a rational design of classifications, a much-favored subject in his time.

The decomposition of complex concepts into the simple ideas constituting them was one of the pillars on which his analytical method rested; it became the backbone of his nosography. He believed that only refined classifications can secure stability to medicine as a science. A logical and systematic distribution, he stated, presupposes a constant order of the matter treated and its being subjected to certain general laws. Diseases wrongly conceived as departures or deviations from nature do have this character of stability, since their histories, as traced by the ancients and moderns, are similar provided one does not disturb the course of nature. Does not careful and repeated observation suggest that diseases are transitory changes of vital functions manifesting themselves by external signs with a constant uniformity of their basic features and an endless variety of their secondary ones? He adopted symptoms as first principles of classification; he added to them the structures and functions of the organs, those of identical tissues (membranes) regardless of their different sites in the body, trusting to avoid thereby changes and instability; nevertheless, he wanted to leave room for future modifications and he wanted classifications to remain flexible.

As a nosologist, Pinel wanted to take advantage of the progress made in his own days by the natural sciences, physics, chemistry, and botany; he included moral philosophy. In brief, he wanted medicine to become a branch of natural history. Posterity did not fail to do justice to this view, though it remained unknown that Pinel was its first apologist and that it was he, the alienist, who anticipated the major role we ascribe today to the basic sciences in our curriculum and training.

In the same book he strove for a definition of medicine. Genuine medicine, he said, is based on principles; it rests less on the prescription of drugs than on the profound knowledge of diseases which has been gained by observationally minded physicians of all eras and which alone should lay the groundwork for public instruction.

To Pinel, observational medicine was synonymous with Hippocratic medicine. His *Nosographie* carries an opening chapter on methods of investigation and observation in medicine; in this chapter he offers a sketchy outline of the march of medical history which is traced as a conflict of ever-changing doctrines and, more particularly, as the ever-renewed struggle between Hippocratism and Galenism, the latter being characterized and condemned by the author for its sophisticated and speculative structure. Pinel considers and praises as true highlights in medical history those periods in which the physician remained faithful, or returned after centuries of barbarism and ignorance, to genuine Hippocratism. He cites Alexander of Tralles (sixth century), T. Sydenham (1624-1689), and G. Baglivi (1668-1706) as foremost representatives of genuine Hippocratism, which was always understood by him to be the glory of our art and the true model of an intrinsically observational and purely descriptive approach towards disease, thereby justifying itself as a branch of natural history, the rise of which in Pinel's day was witnessed by him with delight.

Observation emerges from Pinel's writings as the common link between the two main pillars on which his thought rests, one being Hippocratism, the other being sensualism. By adopting the former he paid tribute to the ancients and to the best medical tradition; by adopting the latter (sensualism), he acknowledged his debt to the ruling philosophical doctrine of his own era and to the teaching of Locke and Condillac.

It remains true, however, that Pinel did not analyze observational thought, and that he did not trace the various intuitive and conceptual constituents of man's observational power; in brief, that he did not outline a true *method* of observation. He simply relied on the sense organs, leaving unfinished the task of constructing and organizing a coherent body of experience out of sense perceptions. So strong was Pinel's sensualistic thought that he recommended "wise caution in trying to reach general ideas and refraining from giving reality to abstract terms"; in contrast, he requested strict faithfulness in descriptions, unequivocal and uniform names, simple and constant classifications based on the structural relations or organic functions of the parts. Pinel was in full possession of the epistemological problems involved in observation. In a sense, he even anticipated future developments and the work of the great French physiologist and philosopher, Claude Bernard, by reaching the idea of experimental medicine, not to take shape until a century later. Experimental medicine consists, Pinel concluded, in careful and *repeated* observation, and in distinguishing between effects of a general and those of an individual nature, thereby paying attention to the constitution of the individual, the influence of the seasons, climates, and age (i.e., again, to factors significant in Hippocratic medicine). Thus, he saw no rupture between ancient and modern medicine, no fundamental difference between observation and experimentation, the former merging into the latter and experimentation ultimately being nothing but observation made under special conditions and restrictions. It thus becomes intelligible that he repeatedly designated the Hippocratic method as an analytical one, though an eminent contemporary medical historian wants to draw a sharp distinction between the Hippocratic, as a more holistic and more synthetical method, and the analytical one, proceeding by fragmentation.

Prefatory Statement to the English Translation of the Introduction to the First Edition of Pinel's "Traité"

There seems to be no published English translation of the introduction to the 1801 (An IX) edition of Pinel's *Traité médico-philosophique sur l'aliénation mentale*. The introduction to the 1806 English translation by D. D. Davis is not a translation of Pinel's introduction; though it paraphrases certain passages from that introduction, it is largely the work of the translator himself. The introduction translated in *A History of Medical Psychology* by Gregory Zilboorg and G. W. Henry as "Introduction to the First Edition" is actually the introduction to the second (1809) edition. In the French original of the 1809 edition it is indeed entitled *Introduction à la première édition*, but it is by no means identical with the earlier work. Each contains many passages not found in the other.

For this reason we have considered it advisable, if not imperative, to present for the first time a complete translation of the introduction to the 1801 edition, which is generally considered the first.

A Note on the Introduction to the First Edition of Pinel's "Traité"

We consider the introduction to be among the most significant and instructive parts of Pinel's medico-philosophical treatise on mental alienation. From the outset, the *philosophical* and *universal* meaning of the whole work is brought to the fore by the author: "I am publishing this work," Pinel said, (because it was) "demanded equally by the need for new progress to be made in the general history of the human mind and in medical science." Thus was substantiated and justified the opening sentence of the introduction, which reads as follows: "The progressive course of insight into the nature and treatment of mental alienation is wholly related to that followed for other diseases and is in accordance with the degree of advancement of the civilization of nations." For the first time in medical history, the barriers were torn down isolating the history of mental diseases and diseases in general from the evolutionary stages of civilization or, in more daring terms, isolating the insane from his normal fellow human beings. *Thus were embraced both the mentally sick and the normal individual as the two members of greater mankind, the alienist appearing side by side with the alienated individual on the ground of the same humanity and the same human mind.* It was only logical that the next sentence of the introduction carried a polemic stigmatization of "narrow empiricism" and the "so-called specifics."

The introduction carries a *historical* sketch. But the latter is not a history of psychiatry in its traditional and narrative setting so much as the history of the symptoms, the diagnosis, the prognosis, and the therapy of mental disorders. The reader cannot escape the impression that it was the *changing concepts of mental alienation* which were on Pinel's mind when he traced the fate suffered by the insane over the centuries under the impact of and in accordance with, "the degree of advancement of the civilization of nations." Again, the philosophical character of the whole treatise is reflected by the meaning of the term and concept of history as applied by the author. It is obvious that the history understood as that of changing concepts needs *a fundamental principle* by which the changing concepts of mental alienation can be brought into a coherent line and system. It is *observation* which emerges from Pinel's texts as such a principle, appearing, disappearing and reappearing during the ages. But it is also observation which allows our author to revive the *Hippocratic tradition* and thus to emphasize the sources of his views on mental alienation in their historical setting as traditionally conceived. We also understand the scope of Pinel's thesis, conceived on historical grounds, that by means of observation some new ideas were added to the doctrine of mental alienation. Pinel here listed an example of an anticipated psycho-pharmacology which took its final shape with the experimental auto-observations made with hashish by Moreau de Tours, that brilliant pupil of Esquirol, himself a pupil of Pinel.

The introduction not only reveals the philosophical and universal nature of the treatise and Pinel's view on mental alienation, but appears to be an anticipation of that pathogenic thesis of Pinel, who saw *the ultimate sources of mental alienation in the human passions* and who repeatedly referred to this view in his treatise as his fundamental doctrine. It is of greatest importance that in the introduction he considers human passions as *simple phenomena of animal economy*, with no idea of morality or immorality, and in their simple relation to the basic principles of our being, upon which they can exert salutary or harmful effects. He referred to Crighton as his predecessor in this interpretation. But when mentioning the physical effects of the passions, he did not refer to Cureau de la Chambre (54), that philosophically minded seventeenth-century physician, author of *Les Caractères des Passions*, who wanted to "depict" passion, to paint the portrait of it, comprising physiognomy, attitude, gestures, gait; in brief, a physical as well as a mental portrait.

The numerous anticipations to be found in the introduction of Pinel's mature thought and final views on mental alienation should not prevent us from overlooking *a strange omission* in the text of the introduction to the first edition: that of the term *moral treatment*, perhaps the most crucial concept of Pinel's entire work. The term appears, however, towards the end of the so-called "Introduction to the First Edition," found in the second (1809) edition. Are we to conclude that the conception and formulation of Pinel's crucial thought underwent its final maturation in the interval between the publication of the first and second editions?

It remains true, however, that the contemporary translation of the 1801 edition of Pinel's treatise on mental alienation already contains a chapter on the moral treatment of insanity. Observation and experience are recalled as the basic methods of treatment common to all civilized nations; but the loss of a friend, who became insane through excessive love of glory, is introduced as a dramatic prelude to the author's discovery of the principles of moral treatment. The inaptitude of pharmaceutic preparations to a mind elated, as his was, with a high sense of its independence, enhanced Pinel's admiration of the judicious precepts of the ancients, and made him regret that he had it not then in his power to put them into practice. The materials upon which his principles of moral treatment are founded, are formulated as follows:

> ... I devoted a great part of my time in examining for myself the various and numerous affections of the human mind in a state of disease. I regularly took notes of whatever appeared deserving my attention; and compared what I thus collected with facts analogous to them that I met with in books or amongst my own memoranda of former dates.

Introduction to the First Edition of Pinel's "Traité"

"Q" The progressive course of insight into the nature and treatment of mental alienation is wholly related to that followed for other diseases and is in accordance with the degree of advancement of the civilization of nations. From the earliest times a narrow empiricism has encouraged the adoption of so-called specifics, whose virtues have been exaggerated and whose methods of administration have been infinitely varied to assure their success. The often fabulous origin of these medications, the long list of detailed and trivial instructions for their use, the haphazard gropings, could hardly fail to arouse the suspicions of observant minds. And as a consequence the true foundations of science were laid, that is to say, the study and the first sketches of a description of mania, knowledge which must of necessity come before any use of remedies. Would it have been possible not to recognize at the same time how powerful was the influence of psychical (moral) and physical treatment in effecting in many cases the cure of the insane? But soon afterwards these sound principles came to be lost throughout the centuries of

"Q" ignorance and barbarism, to reappear feebly at the renascence of science and literature in Europe. Then they translated, they commented upon what was most judicious in the writings of the Greek and Latin authors on mania, but they confined themselves to a superstitious respect, instead of walking in the footsteps of these models. Subsequently there were new digressions from the true path of observation as a result of the love of systems and a misunderstood application of other sciences to medicine. The example and the errors of the past, the false trails that have been blazed, and the strict and methodical course followed in all branches of natural history now oblige us to take up again, in the study of mania, the thread of observation relinquished for so many centuries; and it is with this in view that I am publishing this work, demanded equally by the need for new progress to be made in the general history of the human mind and in medical science.

To prescribe hellebore internally for the cure of mania or other chronic diseases, to know how to choose it, prepare it, and direct its use; this was in ancient Greece the masterpiece of human sagacity, or rather of the most painstakingly compounded empiricism. Some of these precepts seem wise, others petty and superficial and verging on popular prejudices or superstitious ideas. Which was to be preferred—hellebore from Mount Oeta, that from Galatia, or that from Sicily? Other serious subjects for discussion were the food to be taken the day before the administration of the hellebore, the preceding state of emptiness or fulness of the stomach, and the beverages likely to promote its emetic action. There was often extreme difficulty because of the violent intractability of the patients, and how many innocent ruses or artifices were necessary to disguise the drug or combine it with food! Moreover, for the most skilful physicians, the art of correcting or tempering the too energetic or, rather, noxious action of this plant, the precautions to be taken according to individual constitution or the stages of the disease, were subtleties of practice.* But what a triumph of the ingenious sagacity of the physicians of that time was the discovery of certain procedures intended to assure the success of the remedy: repeated washings of the mouth, strong odors, various positions of the body, massage of the extremities! Should there

* For these details consult the articles "Hellebore" and "Helleborism" which I contributed to the *Encyclopédie méthodique par ordre de matières*. (Pinel's footnote.)

"Q" be danger of suffocation, a spasmodic tightening of the throat, a violent cough, syncopes, delirium—then all the subtleties of helleborium were deployed: balancing in suspended beds, fomentations, enemas, use of sternutatories, and innumerable expedients to enhance the efforts of the stomach and bring about cessation of the symptoms.

Hippocrates appears, and an eternal barrier is raised between the empirical use of medications and true medical science, by which I mean the thorough exploration of the nature and course of diseases. The immense field open to his investigations did not permit him to hold specific views on mania, but he provided a general example of the most faithful descriptive method, and men equipped to appreciate it took it as a model in their first sketchings of the history and treatment of mental alienation.

Nothing is more judicious than what Aretaeus has passed on to us concerning the distinctive features of this nervous disorder, its tendency to relapses, and the degree of physical and mental excitation that it produces, though he somewhat overstated the extent of its influence on the supposed knowledge of the science and the fine arts. The precepts given by Celsus carry still more directly the quality of immediate usefulness for the cure of the insane and of a certain disposition to be an observer of their aberrations: rules for guiding them or for rectifying, in certain cases, their false ideas; indications of the means of restraint to be used at times, or ways of kindness and gentleness so often suitable for disarming them; explicit rules for sustained physical exercise and heavy labor; such are the views that he presented, views whose salutary effect the experience of all times has not ceased to confirm. Why should he be cited as the authority for the harsh treatment and acts of violence which he sometimes deems necessary for promoting the cure of mania? Caelius Aurelianus, so inferior to Celsus in elegance and purity of language, seems also to have aspired to glory in his article on mania; the precipitating causes of this disease, its precursory signs, and its distinctive symptoms are carefully noted in this part of his work. He recommends that the insane be shielded from too intense sense impressions; he proceeds to the measures of surveillance suitable for correcting their errors, and he indicates two pitfalls to be avoided by those in charge of them: unlimited indulgence and repellent harshness. The same author indicates the proper mean to be observed between these two

"Q" extremes: the happy talent for adopting with the insane, as the occasion demands, all the outward show of impressive gravity or the simple tone of true sympathy; for winning their respect and esteem by frank and open conduct; for inspiring in them both affection and fear—skills for which certain moderns have been given credit but whose source I indicate here.

It is astonishing that principles so enlightened and so fertile in useful applications should not have shown further development during the long centuries following, especially in the regions of Greece and Italy where insanity is so prevalent and recurs in such varied forms. But the solution of this problem is easy and is found in a brief reflection upon the general course of the human mind. The talent for observation, left to itself, a stranger to intrigue and the art of gaining prestige, is readily appreciated by people of taste and wins the veneration and esteem of enlightened men of all times and all places; an impact upon the minds of men in general, a striking popularity is most often the result of the brilliant qualities of new systems, of a rare skill in showmanship. Galen had this advantage over the observers of whom I was just speaking, and this is doubtless one of the greatest obstacles encountered by the branch of medicine dealing with mental alienation.*

Galen's continual struggle against the various sects (dogmatists, methodists, empiricists, eclectics), his ambition to emulate Hippocrates himself and reign over the schools, his talent for prog-

---

* The following story makes one regret that Galen never devoted himself to the study of mental alienation in particular, since it displays a rare wisdom in discovering a hidden psychical disturbance.

Galen was called to see a lady who was sleepless every night and in continuous agitation; he asked her several questions in order to trace the origin of the malady. Far from giving an answer, the lady turned her head away and covered herself with a veil as though she wanted to sleep. Galen retired; he thought that she was melancholic or affected by some secret sorrow; he postponed further examination until the next day. But on this second visit the slave on duty stated that his mistress would not appear. Galen again retired, came back a third time and again was dismissed by the slave, who asked him not to torment his mistress any longer, since, on the second visit, she had got up to bathe and to take some food. The doctor cautiously did not insist; but he came back the following day and, in a private conversation with the slave, he learned that the affection had its roots in a profound sorrow. At the very moment that he looked at the lady, the name of the actor Pylades, pronounced by a person returning from a play, produced a change in her color and facial expression. The pulse appeared accelerated; this did not happen when at that time or on the following occasion the name of another dancer was pronounced; the object of the lady's passion was no longer in doubt. (Pinel's footnote.)

"Q" nosis, approaching the miraculous, and his study of anatomy left him neither the time nor the inclination to devote himself exclusively to a particular doctrine, and the sway that he has ever since held over the minds of all those who dedicated a sort of superstitious cult to him, which is to say, almost everyone occupied with medicine in Europe, Asia, and Africa for more than sixteen centuries, has diverted attention from the study of mental alienation.

The disputes raised between Galenism and a false chemistry applied to medicine gave rise to much animosity without advancing the wisdom and sureness of the human mind, and mental alienation was merely the subject of feeble compilations lost, so to speak, in general systems of medicine filled with meaningless words and the sterile language of the school. Sennert, Rivière, Plater, Heurnius, Horstius and others thought that in repeating emulously words sanctioned by usage (*distemper of the brain, diagnosis, prognosis, therapeutic indications, etc.*), they had said everything and explored everything: and they profited by their authority as professors to propagate their doctrine on this point as on others and to win the admiration of their numerous disciples, who were always eager to flatter them and share in their glory. Nothing seemed easier, according to their fine and erudite explanations, than to cure insanity. Its cause was without doubt a *fiery and malign indisposition of the spirits,* or a humor, which had to be prepared by preliminary medication so that it could be driven out; it was, according to others, a peccant matter which it was necessary to draw out of the brain and the heart, subject to skillful alteration, and eliminate directly as superfluous or harmful. All nature seemed to contribute to these learned operations by producing at hand innumerable drugs, some endowed with *cold and humectant qualities to dilute the black bile, others designed to follow them as more or less active evacuants,* and it is easy to imagine that hellebore was by no means forgotten. There were introduced as auxiliary measures the internal use of certain substances to fortify the heart and brain, as well as the use of narcotic powders. Externally, epithems were applied to the head, the heart, or the liver, as Hernius says, to *recreate this organ.* I pass over in silence the mysterious specifics sanctioned by blind credulity, so worthy to stand beside the complicated prescriptions of Arabian medicine.

One of the first steps taken by the human mind, left to itself

"Q" and freed from the yoke of Galenism, was to add, by means of observation, some new ideas to the doctrine of mental aliena- tion, and it was van Helmont who had this distinction. A sort of overthrow of the mental faculties, which he experienced as a result of simply tasting the root of aconite, struck him with astonishment and wonder. He attempted to trace back to its cause the singular illusion which made him be- lieve for two hours that the seat of understanding was in the precordial region. The phenomenon of mania seemed to him to offer a fitting explanation of this occurrence; he re- called that several insane persons, now cured, had felt at the onset of their disease a sort of nebulous vapor which seemed to rise from the hypochondrium to the head and produce there a vivid and dominant idea. This idea, according to Van Hel- mont, invades the basic principles of our being, and in order to promote recovery it is necessary to destroy it or counteract it with another even stronger idea. He recalled the treatment by a prolonged immersion of those suffering from hydrophobia, and the accident which befell a maniac who happened to fall into a deep pond, was pulled out apparently dead, and was then restored to life and to the free use of his reason; from which Van Helmont concluded that even the most intractable mania is by no means incurable. He confirmed this with examples of his own, convinced that there was lack of success only when the immersion was of too short duration. However bold such a procedure may seem, especially in view of recent experiences with those put under water, one cannot fail to see in this article the glimmers of a true talent and views worthy of retention, especially for desperate cases. But why do we find in the same work so many empty declamations or inexplicable oddities, popular prejudices concerning the existence of demons, and the *ineffable virtues of St. Hubert's stole for the cure of rabies?*

The impetus given to almost all the sciences in the first half of this century, and the superior talents of Stahl and Boerhave, who were in charge of the public teaching of medicine and chemistry, gave a new form to both these sciences and brought, especially to the former, the strict approach of the spirit of observation, an enlightened admiration for the ancient authors, and a method hitherto unknown. But the extreme ambition displayed by these two illustrious rivals to spread their doctrines to the exclusion of all others, the immensity of their efforts to promote the advancement of all medical knowledge and to fill

"Q" all scholarly Europe with their renown, made it impossible for
them to explore thoroughly any particular disease; and the insane persons still remained confined in their asylums or se-
cluded in isolated dwellings, with no treatment beyond the
ordinary routine of bleedings, baths, and showers. The doctrine
of mental alienation remained, as before, enclosed within a
system of general medicine, or rather it was reduced to a simple
compilation of what had previously been written. Stahl and
Boerhave confined themselves to reporting some case histories
of mania in compendia, academic transactions, or journals,
adding to them at intervals the results of investigations on the
organic lesions of the brain; but it was done to attract public
interest by some piquant oddity rather than to contribute to
the progress of this branch of medicine. The monographs on
mental alienation published during the last half of this century,
whether in England* or in Germany** had no other virtue
than that of bringing together scattered subjects, elaborating
them in the scholastic manner, and giving rise to some brilliant
hypotheses. I except from this the investigation of Crichton (*An
Inquiry into the Nature and Origin of Mental Derangement,*
etc., London, 1798), a profound work full of new results of
observation, in keeping with the principles of modern physiology, but devoted to the preliminary knowledge of mental
alienation rather than designed to explore deeply the history
and treatment of this disorder. I think that I should give here
an exact idea of the origins, the development, and the effects
of human passions upon the animal economy as this author has
presented them and as they should be known, as the most
common cause of the overthrow of our mental faculties.

Crichton seems to have attained a broad point of view which
the metaphysician and the moralist cannot reach, which is to
consider human passions as simple phenomena of animal economy, with no idea of morality or immorality, and in their simple relation to the basic principles of our being, upon which
they can exert salutary or harmful effects. But can one conceive

---

* Battie's Treatise on madness. London, 1758.—Th. Arnold's observations on the na-
ture, etc. of insanity, 1783.—Harper's Treatise on the real Cause of Insanity, 1789.—
Pargeter's observations on maniac disorders, 1792.—Ferriar's medical histories and re-
flections, 1792 (p. XIX). (Pinel's footnote.)
** Faucett, über Melancholie. Leipzig, 1785.—Avenbrugger Von der Stillen, etc., 1783.—
Greding's Vermischte, etc., 1781.—Zimmermann, Von d. Erfahrungen, 1763.—Weickard's
Philosoph. Arzt., Leipzig, 1775 (l.c.). (Pinel's footnote.)

"Q" of any passion without the idea of an obstacle opposed to the fulfillment of a desire or, in other words, without presupposing an unpleasant sensation from which one wishes to escape or a pleasure one attempts to obtain? Do not these natural tendencies, which are the most powerful motivations of our actions, seem to be relevant to the perpetuation of the species, which indicates a threefold objective to be attained: the conservation of our existence, reproduction, and the protection of the human race in childhood? Among the painful sensations which warn us to attain the first goal we count hunger (the most powerful motivation of the actions of civilized or savage man), the more or less intense anxiety which follows the failure to renew air in the act of breathing, the too great impact of heat or cold which demands clothing and healthful dwellings, the uncomfortable sensation produced by the retention of matter which needs to be eliminated, the discomfort which results from a state of seclusion or a lack of exercise, the feeling of lassitude and fatigue which inspires us to seek rest, the state of suffering produced by an internal or external disease which forces us to seek the help of medicine. Is it not, moreover, with the voice of pleasure that nature calls us to preserve our existence: varied foods to flatter our taste, the delight of enjoying pure air or mild temperature, the agreeable sensation of having eliminated matter which needs to be expelled, general well-being after moderate exercise, the intense enjoyment produced by rest after extreme fatigue, the inexpressible sweetness of existence after a state of suffering or a serious illness? Man is incited by pain as well as pleasure to the propagation of the species, especially when he avoids distorting his desires and obeys only the impulses of nature; this thought has slight need of comment. Finally, what sentiments are keener than the tender solicitude of parents for their children, the anguish produced by the sight of their sufferings, or the inexpressible contentment of seeing them free from pain and danger?

The sensations of pain or pleasure which arise from within or from external agents and which warn man to provide for the preservation of his existence, for the propagation of his species, or for the protection of childhood, impress upon him desires to avoid some sensations and enjoy others. The English author might have added that social life and vivid imagination extend almost boundlessly the sphere of needs related to existence,

"Q" that they bring into it the esteem of men, honors, dignities, riches, renown; and it is these artificial desires, continually stimulated and so rarely satisfied, which, according to the exact accounts from asylum records, often lead to mental derangement. It is this same influence which endows the beloved one with heavenly gifts, causes the lover to see in her the highest degree of beauty, grace, and elevation of character, inspires the most vehement desires and, if there are obstacles, all the furors and despairs of love. An excessive sensitiveness renders equally unbearable the slightest pain and the least deprivation of pleasure, resulting in extreme intensity of desires, and, when these are thwarted, in the most violent passions.* Must we not also include in the analysis of human actions the effects of sympathy considered as involving us in the sufferings of others, when it has become personal, intensified by various circumstances, rendered more active and more forceful** by enthusiasm and by the pain and pleasure principle?

The origin of human passions has just been indicated, but how can one conceive their power to provoke mental alienation if one does not know the history of their effects upon the animal economy? Those which can be produced by a profound sorrow are not the least remarkable: a feeling of general languor, decline of muscular strength, loss of appetite, slowing of the pulse, tightening of the skin, paleness of the face, coldness of the extremities, a very perceptible diminution of the vital power of the heart and arteries, producing a false sensation of fullness, oppression, and anxiety, labored and slow breathing ending in

---

* When our primary desires or our aversions encounter obstacles or fail to be satisfied, says Crichton, there arise from this new desires or aversions which are accompanied by a feeling of pain or pleasure and these are entirely different from those which give rise to primary desires. We experience the feeling of these new desires in the precordial region, and they are sometimes so powerful that they destroy all exercise of cool reason and lead to the highest degree of agitation and disorder. These new desires are characterized by an agreeable or powerful feeling in the precordial region and are called *passions*. Primary desire or aversion is distinguished from passion by a difference in the seat of the physical sensation; desire for food is accompanied by a disagreeable sensation in the stomach, called hunger; desire for drink is associated with a disagreeable sensation in the mouth and the throat. But however intense these desires may be, they never produce the special feeling of a passion, unless there is a combination of the two, as when a man deprived of food comes to fear death. (Pinel's footnote.)

** *Théorie des sentimens moraux ou Essai analytique sur les principes des jugemens que portent naturellement les hommes, etc. par Smith, traduit de l'anglais par S. Grouchy, veuve Condorcet; elle y a joint huit lettres sur la sympathie. Paris, an 6.* (Pinel's footnote.)

"Q" sighs and sobs. Irritability and sensibility are sometimes so reduced that the result is a more or less profound torpor, a comatose or even a cataleptic state.

In a less advanced degree, there is a kind of weariness of repeated sense impressions, extreme avoidance of movement and exercise, sometimes sharp stomach pain, and greatly weakened circulation in the blood vessels of the liver as well as in the abdominal viscera, resulting in marasmus and a state of decline; then the sorrow becomes habitual, i.e., becomes melancholia. In both cases, the end is sometimes an irresistible impulse to suicide, sometimes a mild delirium or a state of rage, but prior to this total derangement several disorders set in: momentary madness, an air of gloom or unsociable misanthropy, altered countenance, shy downcast expression, disturbed and confused ideas, a state of stupor or intoxication, and then, all of a sudden, an outburst of the most violent mania.

The animal economy can be as severely upset by fear and terror as by profound sorrow. Fear which arises from the idea of a more or less remote danger has a generally debilitating effect upon almost all the internal and external parts of the body: less forceful heartbeat, weaker pulsation of the arteries, and as a result of the accumulation of blood in the great vessels as well as of the effect upon the diaphragm, an uncomfortable feeling of fullness, oppression, and anxiety, frequently alternating sensations of heat and cold, regional sweating, especially on the forehead and face, excessive urinary flow, and diarrhea. Terror, which differs from fear only in its intensity and sudden onset, has characteristics of its own: acceleration of the heart beat, spasmodic contraction of the arteries, especially on the surface of the body, resulting in pallor and a sudden distention of the great vessels and the heart, momentary interruption of respiration as if by a spasm of the laryngeal muscles, trembling of body and legs, loss of movement in the arms, which hang limp. The sensation is sometimes so intense that the person falls senseless and speechless. Might not such a disturbance, under certain circumstances, produce the most serious disorders, violent spasms, convulsions, epilepsy, catalepsy, mania and even death (Plater, Shenckius, Bonnet, Pechlin, M. Donatus, Van Swieten)? The result may also be a rush of blood to certain parts, and dangerous hemorrhages, such as menorrhagia, haemoptysis, and apoplexy. Should there occur rapid alternations of hope and terror,

"Q" the debilitating effects of the latter may be counteracted, and unheard-of feats of strength and courage may even result. Terror combined with amazement, such as that produced by loud bursts of thunder, the sight of fire on the horizon, the view of a frightful precipice, of a noisy cataract, or of a burning city, also presents significant variations: fixed gaze, gaping mouth, pallor, sensation of cold over the whole body, relaxation of the facial muscles, and often an interruption of the ordinary association of ideas and dizziness. Extreme avoidance of all forms of discomfort, whether mental or physical, intense reaction against everything that threatens our existence, with an extraordinary increase of strength—such are the characteristics of anger, common to both civilized man and the savage roaming the woods. But among civilized nations how numerous are the causes of these violent affections: avarice, arrogance, bigotry, superstition, love, friendship, desire for fame, desire for conquests! From these arise the transports, the secret acts of vengeance, the oppression, the murders, the acts of bravery and of heroism. Anger is modified by its union with other emotional states. When it is combined with courage, the enemy is attacked openly; when it is combined with fear and cowardice, there is an attempt to surprise him and set traps for him. How many disorders anger can produce when considered from the medical point of view! It presents two remarkable variations: pallor of the face, and a somewhat livid color with a sort of weakness and trembling of the extremities, or else a red and inflamed face, sparkling eye, extreme muscular energy. In the latter case, the blood is pushed violently to the surface of the body, producing burning heat, a strong and animated tone of voice, convulsive and irregular breathing. The return of the blood through the veins to the heart is more difficult; it flows back toward the muscles, imparting to them a new degree of action and strength. Its reflux to the brain and other delicate organs may produce much more serious disorders: violent hemorrhages from the nose, the ears, the lungs, intermittent or continuous fevers, delirium or even apoplexy.* One of the strangest effects of anger is to act upon the secretion of the bile and influence its

---

* Hildan (sixth century) reports a remarkable example of this. A fifty-year-old man, somewhat weak and subject to constipation, engaged in a quarrel with another man and received a light blow on the face, which produced in him an anger so violent that he remained for some time unconscious and seemingly dead. When he came to, he returned home with a violent headache. He took some food which he immediately vomited, and during the night he was stricken with a fatal apoplexy. (Pinel's footnote.)

"Q" quantity and quality, as is attested by the most authentic observations (Hoffman, Sulpius, Pechlin); from this arise violent colics, stubborn diarrheas, sometimes jaundice. The only favorable effect which this passion has ever had is that it has occasionally effected a cure of paralysis—but what a feeble compensation for the numberless ills it may cause! When anger is excessive, sudden exhaustion of muscular or vascular irritability, syncope, convulsions, or even sudden death may occur. Anger rarely terminates in lasting insanity, though it alters in such an obvious way the functions of understanding and temporarily interrupts its free exercise. But how many similarities there are between a transport of anger and an attack of mania: redness of eyes and visage, menacing and furious air, harsh and insulting expression. Is it astonishing that one has been described as the other, with only the idea of duration added?

The analysis of the functions of human understanding has doubtless been greatly advanced by the combined works of the ideologists, but there is another analysis, as yet hardly sketched, in which the participation of medicine is necessary; it is that of emotional states, their nuances, their varying intensities, their different combinations. Crichton gives examples for grief, fear, anger, with indications of synonymity; he does the same for the feeling of joy.

Pleasure, which is one of its first degrees, may arise directly from the possession of an object related to our preservation and happiness, or even from a simple memory which makes it seem to be present; for we recall with interest the scenes of our early years, the follies of youth, the emotions felt in the past of kindliness, friendship, love, learning, esteem. We may refer to the same principle our enjoyment of products of the fine arts, of the reading of refined literature, and of scientific discoveries, for they give rise to mixed feelings, whether of admiration for the author's superiority or of inner satisfaction related to some need created by our education or our way of living.* Should

* Harmony of minds as well as of hearts, of tastes as well as of opinions, in sum, the delight of feeling everything together as well as of feeling everything for each other, only this can, in happiness, satisfy the activeness of love and maintain its raptures, which so often shorten its duration. The pleasures of the mind, of the arts, of virtue, enjoyed in conjunction with the pleasures of the heart, deepen and intensify them; they are even necessary to their duration in our present state of civilization, for they add to them a thousand varied charms, they purify them, make them fruitful, renew them; and they extend them to every age of life. *Lettres sur la sympathie.* (l.c. p. XXXVI). (Pinel's footnote.)

"Q" one list among the feelings of joy those quick flashes of jovial humor, those thrills which cause us to laugh, to sing, to dance, and those which are provoked by plays on words, by lively and unexpected repartee, by grotesque imitations, by bits of satire, as if by a sort of reaction of the brain upon the diaphragm and respiratory organs? What an immense difference between these wild sallies of convulsive gaiety and the calm and deep affections arising from the practice of the domestic virtues, the cultivation of talents and their application to some great object of public usefulness, the imposing and majestic spectacle of the beauties of nature!

Joy in different degrees has very marked effects upon the animal economy and acts as an exciting agent particularly upon the nervous and vascular systems. If it is moderate, it imparts a new energy to the beating of the heart and arteries; the various secretions and excretions are thereby increased, with new acceleration of activity and vigor, a more sparkling glance, a more animated expression, more active and energetic functioning of stomach and intestines, whence the numberless advantages to be attained in the treatment of chronic diseases by participation in moderate physical exercise and wholesome diet; whence the effects of music, the theatre, travel, agreeable companionship. These views have been skillfully put into practice in the treatment of aphonia or loss of speech, paralysis, intermittent fever, spasmodic contraction of the pylorus (Alexander Tralles, Pechlin, Etmuller, Hildan, Loiry, etc.). But sudden transitions from joy to grief, from the pleasure of success to the crushing idea of reverses, from a position of dignity which one has occupied and considered oneself worthy of holding to a state of disgrace and neglect, cause profound shocks, and it is for this reason that arrogance and vanity so frequently give rise to mania. Joy, like all means of nervous excitation, may become dangerous if excessively intense, and may end by producing extreme lassitude, a state of languor, fainting, syncopes, or a fatal apoplexy.

A subject which has been by no means thoroughly explored and which has intimate connections with the history of human understanding, the principles of modern physiology, and the effects of human affections and passions upon the animal economy, demands the most precise definition of all the terms applied to these related fields of knowledge in order to express the complex ideas which they comprise and their numerous

"Q" modifications. This is what Crichton realized quite well, and one can but applaud his efforts to fill this gap in medical science; he subjected to a sort of analysis the principle of our actions and found the source in the primitive impulses which spring from an organic structure. His wisdom was also applied successfully to the different functions of human understanding considered in relation to the disorders which impair their free exercise. It is from this standpoint especially that he described the criteria of attention, perception, memory, association of ideas and judgments, adding some remarks about the aberrations, the diminution, or even the destruction which these functions may undergo, and it is from these standpoints that his work is a contribution to the progress of the doctrine of mental alienation (22, p. XL).

Ferriar set a different goal for himself in his particular investigations on mania. He tried various internal medications one after another, directing their use with a sort of empiricism, without distinguishing the different types of mania and the circumstances which must alter the choice and application of remedies. He followed a course analogous to that of Locher, a Viennese physician, the difference consisting solely in the choice and nature of the medications and the order of their use. The task that Chiarugi* accomplished was to follow always the beaten paths, to speak in a dogmatic tone of madness in general, then to consider madness in particular and to return again to the ancient scholastic order of *causes, diagnosis, prognosis, therapeutic indications.* The spirit of inquiry hardly appears in his works, and among the hundred observations that he published, very few can even provide a basis for conclusive inductions. The scattered data in academic publications** and in the compilations of case histories of diseases concerning the character and treatment of alienation or the organic lesions which are its effect or its cause must be cited again, not as likely to extend the boundaries of medical science, but only as raw materials to

* Della Pazzia en generale ed in spezie. Trattato medico-analitico; con una centuria di osservazioni V. Chiarugi, D. M. Professor di Med, et Chirurg, Firenze, 1794 (21, p. XLII). (Pinel's footnote.)

**Acad. des Sciences, 1705.—Acad. des Scien. de Berlin, 1764, 1766.—Transacs. Philosoph., trad. franc., Paris, 1791.—Act Hafniensia, tom. I, II,—Disput. ad Morb. Hist. aut. Haller, tom. I.—Med. Essays, tom. IV.—Lond. Med. Journal, 1785.— Gerard. Vanswieten Const. Epid. ed. Stoll., 1783, etc. (Pinel's footnote.)

"Q" be put to use by a skillful hand and to form a coherent whole by being related to each other or to other analogous data.

From the first centuries of medicine there seems to have been a continuous conflict between a blind empiricism and the lawful and regular practice of medicine; between those who, either from the limitations of their intelligence or the lures of profit, show an exclusive predilection for certain medications, and a group subjected by legal authority to preliminary courses of study, proofs of capacity, and of knowledge. The choice is doubtless easy in the eyes of sound reason, but public opinion often vacillates, as much as a result of certain successes which the empiricists have the skill to turn to account as of the natural interest which the victim of tyrannical oppression inspires. What intolerance! What insulting scorn has often been heaped upon men, some of whom had talents, others the priceless results of long experience, which would have needed only to be clarified and related to sound principles! These ideas are naturally suggested by the example of mental alienation.

In Germany, England, and France men have come forward who, unacquainted with the principles of medicine and guided only by sane judgment or some obscure tradition, have devoted themselves to the treatment of the insane and succeeded in curing a great many, either by temporizing, by subjecting them to regular work, or by adopting, as the occasion demanded, the ways of gentleness or of forceful restraint. We may cite,* among others, Willis of England; Fowler in Scotland; the custodian of the insane asylum of Amsterdam; Poution, in charge of the insane in the Manosque Hospital; Pussin, superintendent of

---

* Détails sur l'establissement du docteur Willis pour la guérison des aliénés. *Bib. Brit.*, p. XLIV.

Lettre du docteur Larive aux rédact. de la Bib. Brit., sur un nouvel établissement pour la guérison de aliénés. *Bib. Brit.*, VIII.

Description de la maison des fous d'Amsterdam, par le cit. Thouin. *Dédac. Philosoph.*, an 4e.

Observations sur les insensés, par M. Mourre, administrateur du département du Var. Broch. de 22 pages.

Observations faites par le cit. Pussin sur les fous, à Bicêtre le premier nivôse. (C'est un manuscrit de 9 pages que je possede.)

Observations on Insanity, with Practical Remarks on the Disease, and an Account of the Morbid Appearances on Dissection. By John Haslam, p. XLV, London, 1794.

(These footnotes are Pinel's.)

"Q" the Bicêtre Hospital; and Haslam, apothecary of the Bethlehem Hospital in London. The practice of living constantly among the insane, of studying their customs, their various characters, the objects of their pleasures or aversions, the advantage of following the course of their aberrations by day and by night at all seasons of the year, the art of directing them quietly without arousing anger or grumbling, the talent for using with them as demanded a kindly manner or an imposing air and of subduing them by force when gentle methods are not effective, and, finally, the continuous sight of all the phenomena of mental alienation and the functions of surveillance, must necessarily impart to intelligent and zealous men a diversified knowledge and attention to detail which are lacking in the physician who, barring an overwhelming interest, is limited as a rule to fleeting visits. But, on the other hand, can empiricists who lack preliminary knowledge of the history of human understanding, put order and precision into their observations or even rise to a language suitable for expressing their ideas? Can they distinguish one type of alienation from another and define it well by bringing together a number of observed data? Would they ever become able to link the experience of past centuries with the phenomena before their eyes, to contain themselves within the bounds of philosophical doubt in uncertain cases, to adopt a firm and sure course to direct their researches, as well as to arrange a succession of objects in systematic order?

I wish that, in medicine, as is done in physics, chemistry, and botany, some account were taken of sane judgment, natural sagacity and an inventive mind without regard to any other qualification; that there were little question as to whether a man had completed certain customary studies or fulfilled certain formalities, but only as to whether he had fathomed some part of medical science or discovered some useful truth. Practicing medicine for nearly two years in the Bicêtre Hospital made me feel strongly the necessity for carrying out these views in order to bring about some progress in the knowledge of mental alienation. The writings of authors, ancient and modern, on this subject, together with my previous observations, could not show me the way out of a certain narrow circle; and should I overlook what many years of watching the insane and the habit of reflecting and observing had succeeded in teaching a man (Pussin) endowed with common sense, greatly devoted to his

"Q" duties and charged with the supervision of the insane in the hospital? The dogmatic manner of the doctor was abandoned from that time on. Frequent visits, sometimes for several hours during the day, helped me to become familiar with the aberrations, the ravings, and the extravagances of the most violent maniacs. From then on I had repeated consultations with the man who knew best their previous condition and their frenzies. Extreme care was taken to safeguard every demand of this man's self-esteem; when answers were obscure, there was a repeated return to the same subject with different questions. There was no opposition on my part to what was doubtful or improbable in his assertions, but a tacit recourse to further examination to clarify or correct it; daily notes were kept on observed data with no other concern than to increase their number and make them exact. Such was the course that I followed for nearly two years in order to enrich the medical knowledge of mental alienation with all the understanding acquired by a sort of empiricism, or rather to complete the former and bring to the latter the general principles which it lacked. Moreover, an isolated infirmary designated to receive a certain number of insane and epileptics provided me with facilities for other research on the effects of medications and the powerful influence of regimen, varied according to the individual disposition or incidental diseases.

We know how unfavorable to medicine public opinion is, and it would be readily agreed that of all the departments of natural history the most difficult is the art of observing internal diseases and identifying them by their external characteristics. In the study of mental alienation, how could these difficulties fail to be magnified? In the first place, there is a natural aversion to, and a strong repugnance for, those who either frighten us with continual shouts and cries of fury or repel us with rough and savage harshness; others stun us with a sort of disordered and incoherent babbling. If we wish to trace and describe the phenomena of mental alienation, that is, of any injury to the mental or emotional faculties, we shall see only confusion and disorder, and we shall catch only fleeting glimpses which give light for a moment only to leave us in more profound darkness, unless we use as a fixed point of departure the analysis of the functions of human understanding. But is there not then another stumbling block to fear—that of mixing metaphysical discussions and ideological rambling with science based on facts?

"Q" We must, therefore, borrow ideas from these related sciences with a sort of sobriety, taking only those which are the least contested and, above all, considering along with them the corresponding external signs and physical changes. It is no less necessary to be armed with courage and determination against an obstacle of another sort—the touchiness and extreme suspicion that the insane generally display towards everything around them, which often drives them to dissemble or to condemn themselves to a taciturnity which one cannot overcome. It would be awkward to show them one's direct intention (of observing them and penetrating the secret of their thoughts) by various questions concerning their condition, for as long as they retain the slightest discernment, the fear of betraying themselves inspires in them a sort of reserve and constraint which makes them appear altogether different from what they are. They then play a role which can deceive the most clear-sighted eyes and which they drop as soon as they are left to themselves. What shall I say of the melancholics who rave only on one particular subject, and with whom one can converse at length without perceiving the slightest disorder in their functions of understanding? I spare you, finally, all the unexpected and temporary changes which can be produced in the insane, when the primary needs of life have barely been satisfied, by a slackening in service, an object of resentment, or atmospheric variations.

To be acutely aware of the difficulties of a subject is no guarantee of surmounting them, but it is another motive for making efforts to overcome them. One should take little notice of those difficulties related to the study of mania which arise from the repugnance which this spectacle must inspire. One becomes accustomed to it, and, besides, the number of the insane who are in a constant state of delirium and fury is very small—the majority are tranquil or experience more or less prolonged intervals of calm. What an advantage the physician has over all the attendants within the asylum! His ministrations have no other purpose than the relief of the ills from which the insane are suffering; he can hardly fail then to find them most favorably disposed, unless they are in a state of complete aberration. Experience has taught me to approach them with serenity and supreme confidence, and no accident has resulted. My first investigations were at the outset pursued haphazardly; I could

"Q" neither distinguish with precision the various disorders of the functions of the understanding, nor rise to a language appropriate for describing them. The study of the French and English ideologists was thus necessary to provide me with a fixed point of departure and enable me to express the distinct character of the different types of insanity, avoiding, moreover, any controversial subject and any metaphysical discussion. The course followed in all branches of natural history served me as a guide, and I concentrated upon external signs, upon the physical changes which might correspond to disorders of the intellectual or emotional functions.* Thus, the features, the gestures, and the movements which give warning of the imminent explosion of an attack of mania were described. The facial expression which characterizes the attack at its height and in its decline was by no means disregarded, nor were the various forms of the skull associated with disorders of the internal senses, which had become the special object of my investigations. How many devices have been brought into use against the powerful and

---

* A woman, now forty-five years old, and detained in the cells, after having experienced for several years a periodic delirious mania, fell into a state of melancholia whose object and character I shall describe: she sees around her nothing but the effects of magic designed to torment her, and all those who are close to her seem to her to be involved in this deception. For the past six months, another illusion has been added to the first: she believes herself to be pursued continually by a spirit which observes her, penetrates all parts of her body at will, speaks to her and shares her bed. As soon as she has gone to bed, she thinks that she sees a bright light which hurls itself upon her and takes complete possession of her; she claims to feel at the same time a burning heat, sometimes a sort of numbness. This spirit sometimes becomes daring and induces in her the sensations of sexual union; most often the feeling is like the breath of a gentle breeze. She converses freely with it and pretends to have heard it utter distinctly these words: *It is useless to resist; I hold you in my power.* This victim of melancholia sometimes remains still and trembling during these delirious episodes; sometimes her hair seems to stand on end, she utters cries of indignation, and those nearby hear her beseech in a loud and passionate voice the powers that disturb her; at other times, beset by timidity and terror, she gets out of bed, throws herself face down to the floor and gives way to the most fervent prayers.

It is obvious that, in order to describe such a malady, it is necessary to trace the history of the false sensations of sight, touch, and hearing experienced by the patient, as well as the false comparisons and errors of judgment which result from them. We attempted to show her how, as a result of an internal condition and independent of any external agent, such sensations could arise; that the eyeball, for example, pushed towards the external angle of the eyelid can product a sensation of light. We were already combining physical and mental treatment when one day the intern charged with recording this history inadvertently placed his hand upon her bed; from that moment she considered him one of the magicians determined to harm her, so that her mistrust became extreme and it was no longer possible to get her to utter a single word. (Pinel's footnote.)

"Q" sometimes insurmountable obstacles opposed by the extreme suspiciousness and shy misanthropy of certain insane persons, always on their guard against everything that comes close to them. The only way to overcome this is with a tone of frankness, an extreme simplicity, and an affectionate manner. Such were the measures that I took in order to insure the greatest exactness in the facts which I gathered and from which I attempted afterwards to form a logical and methodical whole.

A medical work published in France at the end of the eighteenth century should have a different character from one written in a former era; it should be distinguished by a certain elevation of ideas, a prudent liberty and, above all, by the spirit of order and inquiry which prevails in every department of natural history. No longer should it be dictated by special points of view or by the interests of some powerful body, but by pure and honest philanthropy. I leave it to people of taste to decide whether I have fulfilled this task.

V | Pinel as a Moralist: His Views on the Passions

In contrast to purely evolutionary and genetic contemporary views, I remain, like Baruk, in sympathy with the essence of moral thought which is at the root of our Mediterranean civilization, whether this thought is traced back to a *divinely* revealed source or to an *autonomy* of moral consciousness in which man alone shares and which he must recognize as his responsibility through all his weaknesses and secret maneuverings.

Making use of the Freudian dynamism of repression, Baruk has created a type of psychiatry based upon the role of the repression of this moral consciousness and of the special hostility which results from violation and dissimulation of the truth. According to him (9, p. 20) ". . . this type of psychiatry is found implicit in the work of Pinel, in his concern for protecting the mentally ill against cruelty, mockery, and ill treatment."

Baruk, in an effort to revive the true moral treatment inaugurated by Pinel (but woefully neglected since), asks the psychiatrist to free himself from the prejudice of considering the patient as wholly "alienated"; to make contact with him, to develop sympathy, human respect, and the many emotional forces of which one of the most effective is confidence (10, p. 6). Baruk concludes: ". . . solicitude and sympathy for the disinherited remains one of the best criteria of the worth of a civilization." (10, p. 8).

In our time, the essence of moral treatment is often misunderstood because of an erroneous interpretation of the term "moral." Pinel himself, in the introduction to his *Traité médico-philosophique sur l'aliénation mentale*, exhorted his readers to consider the passions, the sources of mental alienation, "apart from all morality and only as simple phenomena of human life." So the word "moral" is used as opposed to physical or physiological and as synonymous with psychical; it denotes that which is related to the mind and not to the body, that which is of a spiritual or immaterial, and not of a material, order (10). This is why I proposed (in 1951) (44) that moral treatment should be considered as synonymous with psychotherapy. Indeed, if the idea of moral treatment included morality (i.e., virtue or moral conduct) as a constituent, and if consequently the physician under the influence of such an interpretation decided to apply moral precepts automatically or routinely as therapeutic measures, grave consequences would result. Pinel had seen examples of this, for he maintained that "mental disorders become all the more resistant if one attempts to support them with supernatural incentives."

Factors in Insanity: The Role of the Passions in Pinel's Terms

"Q" The history of insanity, being inseparable from that of the human understanding, is necessarily found in a very imperfect state in the writings of the ancients. I have, therefore, felt the necessity of commencing my studies with examining the numerous and important facts which have been discovered and detailed by modern pneumatologists. Upon that basis alone must be established any system of nosology founded in nature of a disease affecting either primarily or secondarily the faculties of the human mind. The powers of perception and imagination are frequently disturbed without any excitement of the passions. The functions of the understanding, on the other hand, are often perfectly sound, while the patient is driven by his passions to acts of turbulence and outrage. In many lunatics, a periodical or continued delirium is united to extravagance and fury. Again, instances are not infrequent of actual dementia or mental disorganization, where the ideas and internal emotions appear to have no connection with the impressions of sense, and to succeed each other without order, and to vanish without leaving any traces of their existence. A still more deplorable condition is that of a total obliteration of the thinking faculties, or a privation more or less absolute of all ideas and emotions: in other words, a state of complete idiotism (4, pp. 135-6).

Passions Defined — No Necessary Connection Between the Specific Character of Insanity and the Nature of Its Exciting Cause. The Role of the Constitution, Physical and Mental, Stressed by Pinel

Pinel defined the passions as unknown modifications of physical and mental sensibility *(sensibilité)* ; their distinct characters can only be assessed by external signs. Opposed to each other as some of them may appear to be, anger, fear, intense pain, and sudden joy are all exhibited by various spasms of the facial muscles, their salient features having been subjected to the most profound study by poets, sculptors and painters of the first order. The trained eye of the anatomist can indicate the muscles which, by their isolated, simultaneous, or successive action, serve in the expression of passions.

"Q" Paroxysms of madness are generally no more than irascible emotions prolonged beyond their ordinary limits; and the true character of such paroxysms depends perhaps more frequently upon the various influences of the passions, than upon any derangement of the ideas, or upon any whimsical singularities of the judging faculty. . . . (4a, p. 19) .

My experience authorizes me to affirm that there is no necessary connection between the specific character of insanity and the nature of its exciting cause. Among the cases of periodical mania which I have seen and recorded in my journals, I find some which originated in a violent but unfortunate passion; others in an ungovernable ambition for fame, power, or glory. Many succeeded to reverses of fortune, others were produced by devotional frenzy, and others by an enthusiastic patriotism, unchastened by the sober and steady influence of solid judgment. The violence of maniacal paroxysms appears, likewise, to be independent of the nature of the exciting cause; or to depend, at least, much more upon the constitution of the individual—upon the different degrees of his physical and moral sensibility. Men of robust constitutions, of mature years, with black hair, and susceptible of strong and violent passions appear to retain the same character when visited by this most distressing of human misfortunes. Their ordinary energy is enhanced into out-

rageous fury. Violence, on the other hand, is seldom characteristic of the paroxysms of individuals of more moderate passions, with brown or auburn hair. Nothing is more common
than to see men with light-coloured hair sink into soothing and
pleasurable reveries; whereas it seldom or never happens that
they become furious or unmanageable. Their pleasing dreams,
however, are at length overtaken by and lost amid the gloom of
an incurable fatuity. It has been already observed that people
of great warmth of imagination, acuteness of sensibility, and
violence of passions, are the most predisposed to insanity. A
melancholy reflection—but it is not less true than it is calculated
to interest our best and tenderest sympathies. . . . (4, pp.
15-16).

Pinel's Classification of the Passions and
Their Etiological Role in Mental Alienation

Neither Locke nor Condillac tried to establish a real classification of passions such as was attempted by authors of the seventeenth
century (Riese, 1965) (54), above all by Descartes, whose classification of passions may be called a genetic one, since he traced their
countless varieties back to the six primary passions of love, admiration, hatred, desire, joy, and sorrow. Locke and Condillac enumerated rather than classified the passions. The same may be said of
Pinel, who in this respect does not seem to be indebted to these two
philosophers. Moreover, the designation of the few passions which
Pinel distinguished carry an unmistakable medical connotation
entirely foreign to Locke and Condillac.

Of those passions which are likely to produce mental alienation
Pinel distinguished several types,* i.e., spasmodic passions, debilitat-

---

* Neither Locke nor Condillac attempted a classification of passions, and these are the
only philosophical authors to whom Pinel was indebted, according to his own and
repeated acknowledgments. Descartes *enumerated* the passions, but did not *classify* them,
though his distinction between simple or primitive (wonder, love, hatred, desire, joy,
and sadness) and composed passions may be said to be a first draft of a classificatory
scheme (Article (69 of *The Passions of the Soul*). A classification of the passions which
could have attracted Pinel (into *passiones ardentes* and *passiones frigidae*) is to be found
in Kant's *Anthropologie* which appeared in 1800. By 1809, Pinel's treatise had gone
through its second edition. There is less than a very remote possibility that Pinel had
read and digested Kant's *Anthropologie*.

ing or oppressive passions, and serene or expansive ones. It appears that this classification was entirely his own. He listed anger as a spasmodic passion and believed an extreme irascibility to be a prelude to mental alienation, particularly in women during their menstrual periods or after childbed. Feelings of horror, fright, and utmost despair were mentioned by Pinel as other forms of spasmodic passions which may precipitate mental alienation. Sorrow, hatred, fear, regret, repentance, jealousy, and envy appear in his classification as debilitating or oppressive passions.

Finally, he listed as expansive passions, likely when intense, to affect the mind, the following: joy, pride, love, and ecstasy, religious or not.

An Example of the Effects of Spasmodic Passions

"Q" A very lively woman, commendable for her domestic virtues, for a long time let herself be carried away by an uncontrolled anger for the most insignificant motives. Almost any occasion— a slight delay in the execution of her orders, the slightest mistake made by the personnel or her children—were succeeded by a violent outburst and a tumultuous scene. This unfortunate impulse lost its momentum with the onset of a total confusion. (3, p. 26).

The Influence of the Passions; Irresistible Propensity to Commit Murder

Condillac has displayed equally his sagacity and profundity in the application of the principles of analytical inquiry to the development of certain mental emotions, such as inquietude, desire, the passions which depend upon agreeable or disagreeable sensations, and so on. But, connected with the history of the affections, there are important facts which it is the exclusive province of medical philosophy to unravel and expose. It is for the scientific physician, particularly, to define the limits of those principles in their respective states of health, disease, or convalescence, to ascertain the circumstances by which they are impaired in their action or carried beyond their natural excite-

"Q" ment, to trace their influence upon the moral and physical constitution, and to point out the various diseases which they may
generate or exasperate.

That the functions of the will are absolutely distinct from those
of the understanding, and that their seats, causes, and reciprocal
dependencies are essentially different, can admit of no doubt.
To bring proofs, therefore, in support of a truth universally
admitted is unnecessary, but, to illustrate the fact, I will just
cite one instance of the exclusive lesion of the functions of the
will. It is that of a maniac whose symptoms appeared totally
inexplicable according to the principles of Locke and Condillac.
His insanity was periodical. His paroxysms generally returned
after an interval of several months. The first symptom was a
sensation of great heat in the umbilical region which was felt
to ascend progressively to the chest, neck, and face. To this
succeeded a flushed countenance, wildness of the eyes, and great
distension of the veins and arteries of the head. No sooner was
the brain itself invaded than the patient was suddenly seized by
an irresistible propensity to commit acts of barbarity and blood-
shed. Thus actuated, he felt, as he afterwards informed me, a
contest terrible to his conscience arise within him between this
dread propensity, which it was not in his power to subdue, and
the profound horror which the blackest crime of murder inspired. The memory, the imagination, and the judgment of this
unfortunate man were perfectly sound. He declared to me very
solemnly, during his confinement, that the murderous impulse,
however unaccountable it might appear, was in no degree obe-
dient to his will, and that it once had sought to violate the near-
est relationship he had in the world, and to bury in blood the
tenderest sympathies of his soul. He frequently repeated those
declarations during his lucid intervals, when he likewise avowed
to me that he had conceived such a disgust with life that he had
several times attempted to put an end to it by suicide. "What
motive," he would say, "can I have to murder the governor, who
treats us all with so much kindness? Nevertheless, in my moments of fury, my propensity acknowledges no respect for his
person, for I would then plunge my dagger in his bosom as
soon as in that of any other man. It is to avoid the guilt of
murdering my friend that I am induced to attempt my own
life." It is easy to see that paroxysms of this nature do not admit
of the application of moral remedies. The indication must there-

"Q" fore consist in their prevention by evacuants or suppression by antispasmodics (4, pp. 83-86) .

Examples of the Effects of Debilitating or Oppressive Passions

A young person of weak character, but cultivated mind, was filled with consternation by the sudden and unexpected loss of the fortune of her family and the death of her father. Her mother, left in despair, lost appetite and sleep and became mentally disturbed. In order to contribute to the necessary costs of a pension, the girl renounced her capital of 800 francs revenues; she was reduced to a life of manual work and saw her hope for a proximate marriage vanish. These accumulated disasters finally absorbed all her intellectual functions and led to a melancholic stupor of which she could only be cured by the most assiduous care and eight months of treatment in the Salpêtrière. . . . (3, p. 29) .

The human race offers, in the interior of domestic life, a perpetual contrast of vice and virtue. While one sees families prosper over many years in order and harmony, others, especially in the lower classes of society, distress the spectator by a repulsive picture of debauchery, dissent, and disgraceful misery! This is, according to my diary, the most abundant source of alienation in mental hospitals. . . . (3, pp. 29-30) .

At times the most cruel events lead to despair and alienation, as in the case of a farmer's daughter who, during the Vendée war, saw her brothers and her parents massacred. Struck by terror and in confusion, she succeeded in escaping the slaughter, finally to find herself abandoned and deprived of all resources (3, p. 30) .

Example of the Effects of Gay or Expansive Passions

I have recently been consulted concerning the condition of a man of a lively character, and great sensibility, but who was

"Q" weakened by indulgence in pleasures succeeded by excessive studies. It was under these circumstances that he became very rich by inheritance. He believed himself to be destined to play a great role in the world and to arrive at all sorts of honors and dignities. Increasingly, he began to spend money and to make rural constructions which became a fertile source of worries and annoyances. His irascibility became excessive; his thought was absorbed by his estates and the supervision which they required. Thereby his sleep became disturbed and he frequently got up in the night to roam in the fields and enjoy the elating spectacle of his new wealth. Symptoms became aggravated and his mental disorder increased. Last winter he returned to town with his mind totally shattered and in the most furious delirium (3, pp. 34-35).

Treatment Old and New of Excessive Excitement of the Passions

In all cases of excessive excitement of the passions, a method of treatment, simple enough in its application but highly calculated to render the disease incurable, has been adopted from time immemorial—that of abandoning the patient to his melancholy fate as an untameable being, to immure him in solitary durance, loaded with chains, or otherwise treat him with extreme severity until the natural close of a life so wretched shall rescue him from his misery and convey him from the cells of the madhouse to the chambers of the grave. But this treatment, convenient indeed to a governor more remarkable for his indolence and ignorance than for his prudence or humanity, deserves at the present day to be held up to public execration and classed with the other prejudices which have degraded the character and pretensions of the human species. To allow every maniac all the latitude of personal liberty consistent with safety; to proportion the degree of coercion to the demands upon it from his extravagance of behavior; to use mildness of manners or firmness as occasion may require (the bland arts of conciliation or the tone of irresistible authority pronouncing an irreversible mandate); and to proscribe most absolutely all violence and ill treatment on the part of the domestics, are laws of funda-

"Q" mental importance, and essential to the prudent and successful management of all lunatic institutions. But how many great qualities, both of mind and body, it is necessary that the governor should possess, in order to meet the endless difficulties and exigencies of so responsible a situation! (4, pp. 82-83).

An Instance of Violent Mania Cured by Prudent Coercion: Passions Subdued

A gentleman, the father of a respectable family, lost his property in the revolution, and with it all his resources. His calamities soon reduced him to a state of insanity. He was treated by the usual routine of baths, blood-letting, and coercion. The symptoms, far from yielding to this treatment, gained ground, and he was sent to Bicêtre as an incurable maniac. The governor, without attending to the unfavorable report which was given of him upon his admission, left him a little to himself in order to make the requisite observations upon the nature of his hallucinations. Never did a maniac give greater scope to his extravagance. His pride was incompressible and his pomposity ridiculous. To strut about in the character of the prophet Mahomet, whom he believed himself to be, was his great delight. He attacked and struck at everybody that he met with in his walks, and commanded their instant prostration and homage. He spent the best part of the day in pronouncing sentences of proscription and death upon different persons, especially the servants and keepers who waited upon him. He even despised the authority of the governor. One day his wife, bathed in tears, came to see him. He was violently enraged against her, and would probably have murdered her had timely assistance not gone to her relief.

What could mildness and remonstrance do for a maniac who regarded other men as particles of dust? He was desired to be peaceable and quiet. Upon his disobedience, he was ordered to be put into the strait jacket and to be confined in his cell for an hour, in order to make him feel his dependence. Soon after his detention, the governor paid him a visit, spoke to him in a friendly tone, mildly reproved him for his disobedience, and expressed his regret that he had been compelled to treat him

"Q" with any degree of severity. His maniacal violence returned again the next day. The same means of coercion were repeated. He promised to conduct himself more peaceably, but he relapsed again a third time. He was then confined for a whole day together. On the day following he was remarkably calm and moderate. But another explosion of his proud and turbulent disposition made the governor feel the necessity of impressing this maniac with a deep and durable conviction of his dependence. For that purpose he ordered him to immediate confinement, which he declared should likewise be perpetual, pronounced this ultimate determination with great emphasis, and solemnly assured him that, for the future, he would be inexorable.

Two days after, as the governor was going his round, our prisoner very submissively petitioned for his release. His repeated and earnest solicitations were treated wth levity and derision. But in consequence of a concerted plan between the governor and his lady, he obtained his liberty on the third day after his confinement. It was granted him on his expressly engaging to the governess, who was the ostensible means of his enlargement, to restrain his passions and by that means to screen her from the displeasure of her husband for an act of unseasonable kindness. After this, our lunatic was calm for several days, and in his moments of excitement, when he could with difficulty suppress his maniacal propensities, a single look from the governess was sufficient to bring him to his recollection. When thus informed of impropriety in his language or conduct, he hastened to his own apartment to reinforce his resolution, lest he might draw upon his benefactress the displeasure of the governor, and incur for himself the punishment from which he had just escaped. These internal struggles between the influence of his maniacal propensities and the dread of perpetual confinement, habituated him to subdue his passions and to regulate his conduct by foresight and reflection. He was not insensible to the obligations which he owed to the worthy managers of the institution, and he was soon disposed to treat the governor, whose authority he had so lately derided, with profound esteem and attachment. His insane propensities and recollections gradually, and at length, entirely disappeared. In six months he was completely restored. This very respectable gentleman is now indefatigably engaged in the recovery of his injured fortune (4, pp. 103-106) .

In the Greatest Number of Instances, Especially of Accidental Mania Originating in the Depressing Passions, the Experiences of Every Day Attest the Value of Consolatory Language, Kind Treatment, and the Revival of Extinguished Hope

"Q" A young man, already depressed by misfortune, lost his father and, a few months after, his mother, whom he tenderly loved. The consequence was that he sunk into a profound melancholy, and his sleep and appetite forsook him. To these symptoms succeeded a most violent paroxysm of insanity. At a lunatic hospital, whither he was conveyed, he was treated in the usual way by copious and repeated blood-letting, water and shower baths, low diet, and a rigorous system of coercion. Little or no change appeared in the state of the symptoms. The same routine was repeated, and even tried a third time without success, or rather with an exasperation of the symptoms.

He was at length transferred to the Asylum de Bicêtre, and with him the character of a dangerous maniac. The governor, far from placing implicit confidence in the accuracy of this report, allowed him to remain at liberty in his own apartment, in order more effectually to study his character and the nature of his derangement. The sombrous taciturnity of this young man, his great depression, his pensive air, together with some broken sentences which were heard to escape him on the subject of his misfortunes, afforded some insight into the nature of his insanity. The treatment most suitable to his case was evidently to console him, to sympathize with his misfortunes, and, after having gradually obtained his esteem and confidence, to dwell upon such circumstances as were calculated to cheer his prospects and to encourage his hopes.

These means having been tried with some success, a circumstance happened which appeared at once to give countenance and efficiency to the consolatory conversations of the governor. The patient's guardian, with a view to making his life more comfortable, now thought proper to make small remittances for his use, which he promised to repeat monthly. The first payment

"Q" dispelled, in a great measure, his melancholy, and encouraged him to look forward to better days. At length, he gradually recovered his strength. The signs of general health appeared in his countenance. His bodily functions were performed with regularity, and reason resumed her empire over his mind. His esteem for the governor was unbounded. This patient, who had been so egregiously ill-treated in another hospital, and consequently delivered to that of Bicêtre as a furious and dangerous maniac, is now become not only very manageable, but, from his affectionate disposition and sensibility, a very interesting young man (4, pp. 101-102).

VI
Pinel's Moral Treatment: The Original Meaning of Moral Treatment "(Traitement Moral)"

To reach an intelligible and faithful interpretation of the term and concept of moral treatment (*traitement moral*), the reader must try to assimilate the meaning which the term is given in the French language in general and in the terminology of Pinel in particular. In fact, the term has more than one meaning. The specifically ethical significance is usually referred to, and at all times the conduct of life according to rules emerges as the most widely adopted criterion of moral qualities. Viewed from this angle, the term has an exclusively human connotation, presupposing even human liberty according to the philosophical views adopted by the writers of the fifth edition of the *Dictionnaire de l'Académie Française*, which may be said to reflect the views and language of their great contemporary, Pinel. But the French language has never restricted the meaning of the term "moral" to ethics. The fifth edition of the *Dictionnaire de l'Académie Française*, which appeared in 1825 (i.e., in the lifetime of Pinel), lists as moral virtues (*vertus morales*) those which are rooted in reason alone (*"celles qui ont pour principe les seules lumières de la raison"*). In a still larger sense, the same dictionary defines the term as the opposite of physical, illustrating this extended meaning by quoting the following sentence: *"Le physique influe beaucoup sur le moral, et le moral sur le physique"* (the body strongly influences the mind and vice versa). In modern French the term is also used synonymously with courage (*remonter le moral*), while the use of the term in the fifth edition of the *Dictionnaire de l'Académie Française* as an indication of a greater probability (*certitude morale*) can be considered as obsolete. In which sense did Pinel use the word?

He used the term and concept "moral" as major themes in three different chapters of his *Traité médico-philosophique sur l'aliénation mentale* (3), each time qualifying the term individually, either by definitions or, more frequently, by illustrative examples. When trying to convey to his readers the physical and psychical criteria of mental alienation (*les "caractères physiques et moraux de l'aliénation mentale"*), he referred to his method as an historical exposition of the various disorders of understanding and will (*"l'exposition historique des diverses lésions de l'entendement et de la volonté"*) (3, p. 56); he thus gave a wide opening to a philosophical use and interpretation of the term, qualifying this method as a moral one, with use and interpretation deriving their sources from the classification of human knowledge, a favorite theme of the early nineteenth century. But the term was given its narrower and specifically ethical meaning in that chapter in which Pinel dealt with the emotions and conduct of insane people (*"Émotions et affections morales propres aux aliénés"*). Here he yielded much ground to a nontechnical language, the power of which he greatly admired in the writings of the English contemporary alienist, John Haslam. Pinel did not refrain from using such terms as arrogance, maliciousness, and ruthlessness (*rudesse*) in his description of the conduct of insane individuals, stressing, also in nontechnical terms, their outrageous offenses (*outrages*), their shrewdness (*filouterie*), frequent thefts, and destructive and homicidal tendencies. In the chapter in which he laid down the general rules to be followed in the moral treatment of mental alienation, he returned to a purely rational definition and use of the term, calling his method a kind of moral institution for the development and strengthening of understanding (*"une sorte d'institution morale propre à développer et à fortifier les facultés de l'entendement"*) (3, p. 253). It thus becomes intelligible that he called moral revolution (*révolution morale*) (3, p. 256), the final *insight* of an insane individual into the delusional and absurd nature of his experiences. Pinel here remained thoroughly Cartesian, though the use of the term moral for regained understanding and insight was his own. As stated on a previous occasion (46), the purely humanitarian roots of the moral treatment should not be stressed unduly. The method is basically a well-planned and reasoned one, and its emotional component cannot compete with the forceful element of understanding which emerges from the original texts as its most significant criterion. To be sure, humanitarian feelings, patience, firmness, and constant dedication were considered by the eminent French alienist as prerequisites of moral treatment (3, p. 259), which also included *occupational* activities of different kinds according to individual taste, physical exercises, beautiful scenery, and, from time to time, soft and melodious music *("une musique douce et harmonieuse")* (3, p. 260). But the method was primarily designed and intended to reach man at his best, which in the eyes of the writers of late eighteenth and early nineteenth centuries, meant human understanding, intelligence, and insight.

First Approach to the Meaning of Moral Treatment

The reader might not be prepared to learn from Pinel's treatise on mental alienation that it remained an open question whether the analysis of human *understanding* had contributed much to our knowledge of mental *alienation*. Still, when Pinel shifted his interests to the problem of insanity, he was left dissatisfied with the teaching of Locke and Condillac. The intellectual crisis through which he passed at this decisive moment of his career is reflected by the following passage:

> The peculiar character of those unfortunate cases consisted in a few well-marked circumstances. Their ideas were clear and connected; they indulged in no extravagances of fancy; they answered with great pertinence and precision the questions that were proposed to them: but they were under the dominion of a most ungovernable fury, and of a thirst equally ungovernable for deeds of blood. In the meantime, they were fully aware of their horrid propensities, but absolutely incapable, without coercive assistance, of suppressing the atrocious impulses. How are we to reconcile these facts to the opinion which Locke and Condillac entertained with regard to the nature of insanity, which they made to consist exclusively of a disposition to associate ideas naturally incompatible, and to mistake ideas thus associated for real truths? (4, pp. 13-14).

From then on, the analyses of the passions—their variations, degrees, violent explosions and combinations—seemed to have a more immediate bearing on the subject. He disregarded any moral implications and was anxious to study the passions simply as manifestations of human life. Here were sources of misunderstanding and misinterpretations, Pinel indeed calling the passions *moral* causes of mental

alienation and calling his treatment a moral one. But he was very
far from condemning man or the insane individual morally; nor was
his treatment to be understood simply as an instruction in ethics.

Medical Implications of Moral Treatment: Moral Treatment Particularly Insisted Upon by the Ancients: Its Nature and Its Limitations

"Q" To repeat the maxims which were delivered by the ancients
upon the art of treating maniacs with kindness, firmness, and
address, can throw but little light upon the moral management
of insanity. Those precepts are only of partial utility as long as
the nosology of the disease is not established upon clear and
extensive views of its causes, symptoms, and varieties. The influence of seasons and climates, the peculiarities of individual
temper, character, and capacity, together with the precise nature
of the hallucination, are circumstances which must never be
omitted in the study and treatment of mental derangement.
Illuminating histories of the disease, and candid reports of the
indication and application of remedies (whether successful or
otherwise) from men of acknowledged sagacity and experience,
and all with a reference to the circumstances above enumerated,
might, perhaps, in time contribute to place this branch of the
healing art on a level with its kindred pursuits (4, pp. 48-49).

The Experimental Character of Moral Treatment

Pinel did not gain lasting fame merely because he adopted the
doctrines of Locke and Condillac or because he applied their "analytical method" to the study of mental alienation. Nor did he enter
medical history because he traced mental alienation to the passions
as the ultimate sources. But he stands out head and shoulders in the
early history of psychiatry as the inaugurator of his *traitement moral*.
He did not define it in explicit terms. This may be the reason
why frequently the term has been misunderstood. Another reason

may have to be sought in the misinterpretation of the concept *moral,* which in French usage does not necessarily convey an ethical meaning but may simply have a *psychical* connotation as opposed to a *physical* one. In fact, Pinel was very far from judging his patients and their behavior ethically; in his own terms, i.e., those of the medicine of his era, he intended to look at their violent passions as at subjects of natural history.* The least ambiguous, most faithful translation of his *traitement moral* would be *psychotherapy.***

On one occasion (4, p. 107) he called his *moral treatment "a department of experimental medicine"* and more than once he referred to his often daring, often unpredictable, but always planned methods as experiments. The experiments he had in mind were made by his *thought,* but not by material devices or tools. The aim was to test the patients' reaction to a pre-arranged situation or to a challenging question or statement. Pinel understood experimental medicine*** to be the opposite of crude empiricism, herein anticipating the work of his great countryman, Claude Bernard. *Pinel established faithful and repeated observation as the main criteria of experimental medicine.*

Experimental medicine, he said, ". . . means to observe carefully, faithfully and repeatedly, to list the general and individual results, to consider the individual constitution, influence of the seasons, life period, etc. This is Hippocratic medicine."

The media through which his moral treatment was intended to reach the patient, were the "maxims of enlightened humanity," a

---

* Cabanis, philosopher, physician, politician, contemporary of Pinel, and one of the most significant representatives of eighteenth century medicine, included *moral* problems in his major work *(Rapports du Physique et du Moral)* solely because they are "an essential part of the natural history of man" (13, p. 12a) .

** In 1961, Ivor Kraft suggested psychotherapy as "the modern counterpart" to the term moral treatment. Ten years earlier, I characterized Pinel's *traitment moral* as "a systematic therapy of mental disorders by psychological means" (44) . It was not too fortunate that Kraft included in the meaning of moral treatment the "tender loving care" of institutional parlance (27) . Nor do I believe that Pinel's original texts and intentions justify the conclusion reached by Eric T. Carlson and Norman Dain in *The Psychotherapy that was Moral Treatment* (15) that "moral treatment consisted principally of what we might now call *milieu therapy.*" It remains true that a resourceful psychotherapist of Pinel's caliber may *occasionally* turn to "tender loving care" or *milieu therapy,* none of which, however, reach the *full* scope of moral treatment in its authentic meaning. Repeatedly, I warned the reader not to interpret the latter in terms of ethics. It remains true, however, that Pinel's treatment made a strong appeal to moral concepts such as respect, self-esteem, and dignity for both patient and physician.

*** The experimental component in Pinel's medical thought was first shown by me in my *Philippe Pinel (1745-1826)* (46) .

significantly eighteenth-century concept. Other media were: powerful impressions, imagination, occasionally intimidation and even coercion, though only reluctantly applied and only in emergencies and in the sole interest of the patient's own safety; it would be impossible to disclose the inexhaustible treasure of Pinel's strategic maneuvers to overcome resistance, stubborn abstinence, or to tranquilize the most furious maniacs.

The concept of and the term moral treatment were entirely his own. He could hardly be expected to name any source from which he might have derived the new concept. Yet, there is to be found in that chapter of his treatise (second edition) which bears the title, "General Precepts to be Followed in Moral Treatment," a significant and lengthy footnote describing the method practiced in ancient Egypt where patience, firmness, and humanitarian feelings characterized the treatment of melancholics.*

But the moral management of insanity, Pinel said, required more than the maxims which were delivered by the ancients upon the art of treating maniacs with kindness, firmness, and address; it required the knowledge of the nosology of the diseases established upon clear and extensive views of their causes, symptoms, and varieties, the influence of seasons and climates, the peculiarities of temper, character, and capacities of the individual, together with the precise nature of hallucination. One thus understands that Pinel was not willing to apply his principles of moral treatment with undiscriminating uniformity to maniacs of every character and condition in society.

Most of the more recent publications on the subject were dis-

---

* "At the two extremities of ancient Egypt, which was then very populous and very flourishing, there were temples dedicated to Saturn to which melancholics flocked, and where priests, taking advantage of their trustful credulity, promoted supposedly miraculous cure by all the natural means suggested by hygiene: games and recreative exercises of every sort were encouraged in these temples; voluptuous paintings and seductive images were displayed on every side to the patients; the most pleasing songs, the most melodious sounds often charmed their ears; they walked in flowery gardens, or in groves exquisitely adorned; sometimes they were taken in decorated boats to breathe fresh and salubrious air upon the Nile while music played; sometimes they were conducted to gay islands, where, under the symbol of some protective divinity, they were provided with new and ingeniously devised spectacles and select company. Finally, much time was devoted to comic scenes and grotesque dances, a system of diversified amusement with a religious undercurrent. With an appropriate and scrupulously observed diet, with journeys to reach the sacred places, the continuous festivities deliberately provided along the way, hope fortified by superstition, the skill of the priests in supplying favorable diversion and in banishing sad and melancholy thoughts — could all this fail to relieve pain, calm anxiety, and effect salutary changes, which the priests were careful to turn to account in inspiring confidence and establishing the prestige of the tutelary divinities?" (3, pp. 259-260) .

missed by Pinel as "mere advertisements of lunatic establishments under the superintendence of their respective authors." Nor did Pinel feel indebted to his contemporaries for any source of his concept of moral treatment, with at least one exception, i.e., the principles adopted in the famous British Bethlem hospital, where the superintendent, John Haslam, endeavored to win the *confidence* of his patients, to arouse in them feelings of *respect* and *obedience*, and to prevent them from experiencing fear and contempt. The new shining models of moral treatment could not prevent Pinel from reaching, in the introduction to the first edition of his treatise, the following conclusion:

> On every hand there has been neglect of the purely philosophical viewpoint in mental alienation, the knowledge of physical or psychical causes likely to produce it, the differentiation of its diverse types, the exact history of precursory signs, the course and the termination of the attacks (when intermittent), the rules of the inner management of the hospitals, and the precise determination of the circumstances which necessitate certain remedies, as well as of those which render them superfluous; for, in this disease, as in many others, the skill of the physician consists less in repeated use of remedies than in the deeply thought-out art of using them appropriately or of refraining from using them (3, pp. XXIV-XXV).

This conclusion opened the history of modern psychiatry. Etiology, symptomatology, diagnosis, course, and therapeutical indications emerge from this conclusion as branches of that new science from which the nineteenth and twentieth centuries secured their objective and subjective implements. The figure and the achievement of Pinel cannot be captured solely by the conventional and sentimental praise of his humanitarian feelings, for his so-called philosophy embraced the best and most ancient traditions of medicine, which were deeply rooted in the observational spirit of Hippocratic medicine to which, in Pinel's own terms, should be paid eternal tribute. Pinel saw no rupture between ancient and modern medicine, no fundamental difference between observation and experimentation, the former merging into the latter and *experimentation ultimately being nothing but observation made under special conditions and restrictions.* He repeatedly designated the Hippocratic method as an analytical one.

VII | Pinel as a Philosopher

As early as my first paper (1951) (46) devoted to Pinel, to his concept of man and disease, and to his medical thought, I came to the conclusion that some doubt should be cast upon the romantic tradition whereby Pinel figures in the history of civilization and in the origins of modern psychiatry as the sensitive, if not sentimental, apologist of the insane, braving the resistance of the suspicious revolutionary authorities to liberate them from their chains. On the contrary, I advanced the thesis of Pinel as a clinician, a scholar, and a philosopher, shaped and guided by the philosophical tendencies of the eighteenth century, by its analytical and experimental spirit, rather than solely by love of his fellow-man.

Assuredly, no one could fail to recognize the profoundly humanitarian sources of a work that was apparently the manifestation of a fundamentally generous nature, needing no instruction or experience. More than once Pinel refers the reader to humanitarian feelings as the *primum mobile* of his efforts, which afterwards became legendary; he refers him to his quasi-innate views on the inalienable rights of humanity and on crime resulting from the violation of those same human prerogatives. Of these views his biographer, Semelaigne, has retained some authentic expressions. "The uninterrupted use of chains" (62, p. 141) is indeed in the foreground of Pinel's preoccupations and anxieties. So he deplores, in a general way, "the lack . . . of humane principles," (62, p. 142) but particularly "this barbarous and routine custom," (62, p. 141). A whole chapter of the history of humanity and civilization appears before the eyes of the reader of the following sentence: "The insane, far from being culprits who should be punished, are sick persons whose painful condition deserves all the consideration due to suffering humanity, and whose

69

lost reason we should seek to restore by the simplest means" (62, p. 147) . Moreover, one has only to read, first, the description by Pariset, in his eulogy of Pinel, of a public asylum in the days when Pinel was named physician-in-chief of the Bicêtre hospital, and then read afterwards in Pinel's own words his authentic account of his reforms and of the goal he set for himself. It will not be without surprise that the reader will learn from Pinel's lips that these same abuses and violations of human dignity by the use of chains at times appear as simple "disadvantages" which make it difficult, if not impossible, to establish the natural history of mental alienation, a history of great concern to Pinel. Indeed, "How is one then to distinguish the exasperation which is the result of this (treatment) from the symptoms of the disease itself?" He confesses that, "In the Bicêtre hospital for the insane, the history, properly so called, of the peculiar phenomena of mental alienation has been, therefore, the principal object of my investigations, and I have attempted to determine the distinctive characteristics of the various species, the differences between continuous and intermittent mania, the purposes to be accomplished in moral treatment, the rules of surveillance and internal discipline in such a hospital, and finally, certain bases for medical treatment founded solely upon observation and experience."

From this self-analysis, Pinel's figure and work emerge as *far exceeding the bounds of pure humanitarianism* to encompass the goals of a *naturalist,* an *administrator,* a *reformer,* a *clinician,* a *therapist* and, above all, a *philosopher.* The passage just cited is found in the introduction to the great *Traité Médico-Philosophique sur l'Aliénation Mentale.* Rarely does an introduction sum up in one master-stroke with such concentrated force the whole of the author's vocation and methods, which have only to be enumerated, explained, and justified in the hundreds of pages following this preliminary text, which is at the same time a program. Here Pinel displays his talent as a *man of letters* and as an *author,* carrying within himself, as an artist does, the image or vision of his whole work, with all its present and future ramifications, with its successes and its pitfalls. The birth of the complete work will be merely the continuation of a metamorphosis whose different stages will emerge from the seed as do the leaves of a plant from their archetype. The seed, still undifferentiated, does not reveal the future developmental stages, which are not preformed on a minute scale, but which owe their existence to a creative or *epigenetic* act inherent in the seed, but beyond our powers of perception. We have reached the limits of empirical analysis; we have neither the desire nor the ability to invade the metaphysical realm of actual or literary creation.

The name of Montaigne appears among the three favorite authors of the young Pinel; those of Hippocrates and Plutarch are cited at the same time by E. Pariset, the author of a eulogy of Pinel (34, pp. 189-231). And he adds: "Whatever may be the actual diversity of their canvases, these three great painters of human nature have a characteristic in common which distinguishes them from other writers." It is not at all difficult to recognize in this that source of Pinel's work related to the science of man or philosophical anthropology, which is at the root of his concept of mental alienation. This source, then, apparently revealed itself very early and, as one learns from Pariset, in communication with a young friend of Pinel who became his student: *docendo discimur*. The anticipation of the philosophical foundations of Pinel's work (that of the spirit of observation claimed by him time and time again), but above all, the anticipation of his moral treatment, seems to be revealed in the following passage from the introductory chapter ("The Life and Work of Montaigne") of the recent edition of the *Essays of Michel de Montaigne* by Pierre Villey (Presses Universitaires de France, Paris, 1965) (66) : ". . . under the ruins accumulated by Pyrrhon, he (Montaigne) recognized that there remains a solid foundation, and only one, upon which reason can build: the positive fact. He is moving toward a positivism at once flexible and firm; and, as a moralist, it is in himself, above all, that he will seek the certain fact upon which to build his ethics."

It is undeniable that Pinel, to attain the maturity of his mind and work, must have drawn upon the writings of the ancients and those of the eminent French philosophers of the two centuries immediately preceding his, the sixteenth and the seventeenth; but it is the spirit of the eighteenth century which definitely moulded him. So it was that Esquirol, commissioned to make a report upon the proposition to place a bust of Pinel in the hall in which the sessions of the Academy were held, could declare that, "Nourished upon the reading of the ancients, from whose works he had made a large number of extracts, M. Pinel did not repudiate the heritage of antiquity; he enhanced it with modern discoveries . . . he brought to clinical study that spirit of observation and of method which has contributed so much to the perfecting of the natural sciences." In these few lines the eminent pupil painted an almost complete picture of the tradition and the methods followed by his illustrious teacher. It is true that the names of the philosophical authors who preceded Pinel and more immediately formed his thought (La Rochefoucauld, Montaigne, Descartes, Rousseau, Condillac) do not appear in this report; it is the physician especially who is speaking and who is making an historical analysis of the medical work of the alienist, Pinel.

In his description and in his interpretation of mania at its highest degree of intensity, Pinel unmistakably turned to the genuine thought and language of Condillac. It is the impressions produced by the external objects on the sense organs which are believed by Condillac to be the ultimate sources of human knowledge, and it is just these sources, or, in Pinel's terms, the relations to external objects which the insane are unaware of. In other words, the insane person is no longer reached by sensations. But to sense sensations is to be aware of one's own existence (though not yet of that of external objects). The statement that a pure and simple sensation teaches us no more than our own existence occurs in Condillac's *Traité des sensations;* it recurs word for word in Destutt de Tracy's *Idéologie* (65, p. 148) ; and, finally, it occurs in Pinel's *Traité médico-philosophique sur l'aliénation mentale.*

I cannot emphasize strongly enough the continuity of thought and language leading from Condillac to Destutt de Tracy, finally to reach Pinel.

Pinel was neither the first nor the last author whose views on disease were rooted in philosophical doctrines, the technical language of which often reappears in the genuine terms of the vocabulary of the medical authors adopting the particular doctrine. Here is the source of an esoteric terminology and an estrangement among physicians aiming nevertheless at an intelligible interpretation and sound therapy of the same disease.

The State of the Knowledge and Treatment of Insanity in Pinel's Day; The Philosophy of Mental Alienation Explained

"Q" Few subjects in medicine are so intimately connected with the history and philosophy of the human mind as insanity. There are still fewer, where there are so many errors to rectify, and so many prejudices to remove. Derangement of the understanding is generally considered as an effect of an organic lesion of the brain, consequently as incurable; a supposition that is, in a great

"Q" number of instances, contrary to anatomical fact. Public asylums for maniacs have been regarded as places of confinement for such of its members as become dangerous to the peace of society. The managers of those institutions, who are frequently men of little knowledge and less humanity, have been permitted to exercise towards their innocent prisoners a most arbitrary system of cruelty and violence; while experience affords ample and daily proofs of the happier effects of a mild, conciliating treatment, rendered effective by steady and dispassionate firmness. Availing themselves of this consideration, many empirics have erected establishments for the reception of lunatics, and have practiced this very delicate branch of the healing art with singular reputation. A great number of cures have undoubtedly been effected by those base-born children of the profession; but, as might be expected, they have not in any degree contributed to the advancement of science by any valuable writings. It is, on the other hand, to be lamented that regular physicians have indulged in a blind routine of inefficient treatment, and have allowed themselves to be confined within the fairy circle of antiphlogisticism, and by that means to be diverted from the more important management of the mind. Thus, too generally, has the philosophy of this disease, by which I mean the history of its symptoms, of its progress, of its varieties, and of its treatment in and out of hospitals, been most strangely neglected (4, pp. 3-5).

The Need to Meditate upon the Writings of Locke and Condillac

Pinel belonged to that school of philosophical thought known as sensationalism, represented in England by Locke and in France by Condillac. It was the *theory of experience* advocated by these two authors which attracted Pinel as it did so many of his contemporaries; it is this theory which is also at the root of that part of Pinel's view on mental alienation which needs the function of *understanding* as its vehicle and instrumentality. The *passions*, which Pinel claimed repeatedly and vigorously to be the true sources of mental alienation, were given but a minor place in that sensualistic theory of experience.

But the important role ascribed by Pinel to the teaching of Locke for the genesis and structure of his view on mental alienation makes

it imperative to do still greater and historical justice to the spirit
and the letter of Locke's system, which shaped the minds of those
eighteenth-century philosophers and men of letters who prepared
both for the French Revolution and for the coming of a citizenship
no longer tolerant that men, sane or insane, should waste away in
the fetters of prejudice, paralyzing tradition, and cruelty.

Chapter XX of Book II of Locke's *Essay Concerning Human
Understanding* is titled "Of Modes of Pleasure and Pain." The concluding paragraph of the chapter carries the sentence: "I would not
be mistaken here, as if I meant this as a discourse of the Passions . . ."
But the chapter is a very short one and hardly more than an enumeration and descriptive analysis of a few of them (pleasure and pain,
love, hatred, desire, joy, sorrow, hope, fear, despair, anger, envy,
and shame). To grasp the significance assigned to the passions in
Locke's system, we must trace the place where they are first introduced into this system. This, however, is not possible without incor-
porating Locke into the genuine atmosphere and needs of the
eighteenth century and without our *retracing*, though in a sketchy
manner, *the basic tenets of the whole system* that the English philosopher conceived in the seventeenth century. Locke distinguished two
"fountains of knowledge," i.e., the objects of sensations and the
operations of our mind; and from these sources spring all of the
ideas we have, or can naturally have; an idea being defined as "the
object of thinking," be this "*phantasm, notion, species,* or whatever
it is which the mind can be employed about in thinking" (31, Intro.)

As to the first source of ideas, i.e., the *sensations*, they, of course,
depend wholly upon our senses, and are derived by them for the
understanding (31, Book II, I, 3). It is this first source of all ideas
which left on the whole system its well-known imprint as an *experiential* and, more specifically, as a *sensualistic* one.

The second source from which experience furnishes the understanding with ideas, i.e., the perception of the *operations of our own
mind* within us, as it is employed about the ideas it has obtained, is
defined as *perception, thinking, doubting, believing, reasoning,
knowing, willing*, and all the different actings of our own minds.
This source of ideas every man has wholly in himself; and though
it be not sense, as having nothing to do with external objects, yet it
is very like it, and might properly enough be called *internal sense* or,
finally, *reflection*. But here Locke makes a qualifying remark by
which the passions are introduced into the whole scheme. The term
"operations" (i.e. of the mind) is intended by him to be used "in a
large sense, as comprehending not merely the actions of the mind

about its ideas, but some sort of passions arising sometimes from them, such as is the satisfaction or uneasiness arising from any thought" (31, II; I, p. 4). In another passage he reaffirms this thesis by stating that "delight or uneasiness, one or other of them, join themselves to almost all our ideas both of sensation and reflection . . ." The Cartesian dual genesis of the passions—some of them being excited by the objects which move the senses and others by the action of the soul, which determines itself to conceive of this or that object—recurs in Locke's essay, though in less explicit terms. Indeed, by pleasure and pain he intended to understand "whatsoever delights or molests us; whether it arises from the thoughts of our minds, or anything operating on our bodies" (31, II; VII, p. 2). Locke did not, however, reach the Cartesian conclusion that it is precisely the role and functional significance of the passions to fortify and prolong in the soul the thoughts that should be conserved and which, lacking their support, might readily be effaced from it (19, *The Passions of the Soul*, Article 74, p. 310). Nor did Locke consider the instrumental role of the passions at large, with at least one exception, however —that of pain, ". . . the end or use of which he conceded to be to warn us of the harm that many things may do to our bodies, to advise us to withdraw from them, before the organ be quite put out of order, in brief, to preserve our being" (31, II, VII, p. 4). One must conclude that, at least in his discourse on the passions, Locke did not forego *teleological* interpretations.

But what prevented Locke, one might ask, from adopting a design, therapeutical or not, making full *use* of the passions, the instrumental role of which he was approaching, at least in this one significant area? He ascertained man's obligation to fight or to master the passions by simply and dogmatically requesting it from him, without outlining any design that could teach man how to govern the passions or at least assist him in this struggle: "And how much this is in everyone's power, by making resolutions to himself, such as he may keep, is easy for everyone to try" (31, II, XXI, p. 54).

Locke, though a physician, was not concerned with the physical equipment of the passions. Though Descartes' design of this equipment was purely speculative, it provided him with the foundation on which to construct his "general remedy against the passions." We must exercise ourselves, Descartes stated (21, p. 793 Article 211, p. 793), in separating within us the movements of the blood and spirits from the thoughts to which they are usually united. He was not satisfied with the simple advice, but he described a method through which the advice could be put into practice. "When we feel our

blood . . . to be agitated, we should be warned of the fact, and recollect that all that presents itself before the imagination tends to delude the soul and causes the reasons, which serve to urge it to accomplish the object of its passion, to appear stronger than they are, and
those which serve to dissuade it to be much weaker" (l.c.). As
already stated, the methods derived from these considerations are
delay and *diversion;* the only technical and speculative term retained
was that of "agitation of the blood," which makes a minimum demand on physiological thought that is neither trained in observation
nor in experimentation.

It certainly is thought-provoking that Locke, who wanted to rely
on nothing but experiential data, had no concrete device to offer to
man to govern his passions, whereas Descartes, though relying on
purely speculative instrumentalities, was able to design a workable
method to master the passions. Could it be true that it is not from
experience itself that man can expect to learn the mastery of that
reality which he faces when involved in passions?

Still, Locke left to man the power to *suspend* his determination
to master the passions "till he has examined whether the action proposed be really of a nature in itself and in its consequences to make
him happy or not" (31, II, XXI, p. 57), happiness, according to
Locke, being "the utmost pleasure we are capable of" (31, II, XXI,
p. 43), and things being good or evil only in reference to pleasure or
pain (31, II, XX, p. 2.) (Locke here hardly denying *epicurean moral*
thought). It is "the prevalency of some present pleasure or pain
heightened by our feeble, passionate nature" (31, *ibid.*) the "haste
or the precipitancy" in which a wrong judgment is formed "as if it
were a perfect ignorance," which should be checked by understanding
and reason (Locke here being *Socratic* in his moral thought). The
principal exercise of freedom, according to Locke, is "to stand still,
open the eyes, look about, and take a view of the consequence of
what we are going to do as much as the weight of the matter requires"
(31, II, XXI, 69). It is only too obvious that the factor of "suspension" and its antithetic terms of "haste" and "precipitancy" are survivals or revivals of the implements of the *Cartesian* "general remedy
against the passions."

In this area Condillac, Locke's apologist in France in the eighteenth century, remained Cartesian, though in a general sense: he
intended his method to be sharply demarcated from that used by
Descartes, who believed innate ideas, general principles and abstract
notions to be the sources of our knowledge. In contrast, Condillac
considered the ideas reaching us from the senses to be the most simple

ones and to be the raw materials of our knowledge out of which we form, through combination, complex and abstract ideas.

In the introduction to the first edition of his *Traité médico-philosophique sur l'aliénation mentale*, Pinel raises the following questions:

> Should the physician not be familiar with the history of the most violent human passions which are indeed the most frequent causes of insanity? Should he not study the lives of men most famous for their ambition and strivings for glory; their scientific discoveries, artistic achievements, the austerity of their solitary lives, or the extravagances of their unhappy loves? Can we expect a physician not familiar with the writings and doctrines of Locke and Condillac to be able to analyze the manifold changes and distortions of the human mind? Could a physician, treading slavishly the beaten paths, lacking sound judgment and an ardent desire for knowledge, be fully aware and conscious of the true significance of the endless observations he will make? Is the history of mania not linked with all the errors and illusions of credulity, ignorance, miracles, demoniacal possessions, divination, oracles and witchcraft? (3, pp. X-XI).

While there can be no doubt that John Locke was an outright apologist of *medical* empiricism, it still remains an open question as to what extent he may be called an empiricist in a more *general*, i.e., philosophical, way. Recently he has been called (29, p. 21) an experimentalist rather than an empiricist, his reflections on the primary and purely sensory data testifying to the *active* constituent of his exploring mind, which in the genuine conception of empiricism is passive, i.e., the proverbial *tabula rasa* on which the external data or impressions simply leave their imprints. Memory, discrimination, reasoning, judgment, knowledge and faith are cited as criteria of Locke's acting, analyzing, and creative, rather than simply recipient, mind. Locke's active participation in the events of his century are cited to the same purpose. In Locke's authentic terms, knowledge is the perception of the agreement or disagreement of two ideas.

Though nobody would expect Platonic sources in Locke's theory of knowledge, it nevertheless remains true that in Plato's theory of knowledge, as outlined in his *Theaetetus*, sense perception is not the whole of knowledge; nor is perception, even within its own sphere, knowledge at all. As F. M. Cornford (35) says in his running commentary of Plato's dialogue, there must be a mind centrally receiving the several reports of the sense organs and capable of reflecting upon the data of senses and of making judgments. Thus, in both Plato's and Locke's theory of knowledge, it is the *reflection* upon the data of sense which emerges as the criterion of knowledge. In these judgments the thinking mind uses terms like "exists," "is the same as," "is different from"; in brief, one sees reappear in Locke's theory of knowledge the Platonic "common terms" or "ideas." Could it be true that such a resolute *empiricist* as Locke ultimately reached the most *idealistic* concept of the Platonic forms—the criterion of knowledge?

Pinel Questions the Doctrines of Locke and Condillac on Understanding, Will and Desire

There was one area in Pinel's investigations which seemed to resist the *analytical method* and *to threaten the principles of Locke and Condillac* in a more general way. The history of a maniac living under the threat of recurring murderous impulses appeared to Pinel to be ". . . totally inexplicable upon the principles of Locke and Condillac," and led him to declare that "the functions of the will are absolutely distinct from those of the understanding," since the memory, the imagination, and the judgment of this unfortunate man were perfectly sound. Pinel was evidently referring to Locke and Condillac solely as explorers of human *understanding*.

Tracing the genealogy of Pinel's thought from the eighteenth century philosophers and encyclopedists back to its origins in Bacon's classification of human knowledge, we do not find the *will* missing in the table of the "father of experimental philosophy." The division, "Human Philosophy," which has reference to reason as one part of man's basic faculties, is subdivided into "Man as an Individual" and "Man in Society," with the former again divided into the "Undivided State of Man" and the "Divided State of Man," the body and the mind being the two divisions of the divided state of man. The faculties of the mind, which are parts of the divided state of man, are listed as the *understanding* and the *will*. Bacon's interpretation of "that knowledge which considers of the Appetite and Will of Man" at this point merges into a sketchy exposé of moral philosophy, (the inquiry concerning the roots of good and evil being in the focus of Bacon's interest) which culminates in the prescription that "the conservation of duty to the public ought to be much more precious than the conservation of life and being" (8, I, p. 219), a tragic denial of Bacon's own conduct and life. The informed reader of Pinel's treatise learns with more than casual interest that "this faculty of the mind (of "will and election") which inclines affection and appetite . . . may be so well-governed and managed, because it admits access to . . . divers remedies to be applied to it and to work upon it." Religion, opinion, apprehension, affection, custom, and habit are cited as "medicines" of the will. But it was the previously cited observation of a maniac that shaped Pinel's belief that the functions of the will may be exclusively diseased and which led him to confess that "paroxysms of this nature admit not of the application of moral medicines. The indication must, therefore, consist in their prevention by evacuants or suppression by antispasmodics" (4, p. 86). In brief, it was in the area of an irresistible impulse that Pinel experienced the *limits* of his moral treatment and yielded to the application of physical remedies. But he failed to offer a rational explanation of this enigmatic effect of physical treatment on mentality. Here are the limits of Pinel's philosophical endowment.

Locke discussed the will in chapter XXI ("Of Power") of the second book ("Of Ideas") of his *Essay Concerning Human Understanding*. Will and understanding are presented as "two powers in mind or spirit." There follows a rather lengthy discussion of will, liberty, and necessity. We retain from this discussion Locke's sharp distinction between will and desire, a distinction which might open to the student of a comparative historical analysis of our subject the road to a number of nineteenth century concepts, above all to Schopenhauer's view of the will as a metaphysical but unconscious force and of its manifold manifestations in man's life and thought. Desire is defined by Locke as "an uneasiness of the mind for want of some absent good." It is the *uneasiness of desire* that determines the will and is "the spring of action." Similar statements were made by Condillac. It is no great step from these assertions to the declaration of the Freudian pleasure principle, the preconcept of which may thus be traced (disregarding the ancients) to John Locke, who forcefully affirmed that man is not moved to act by the sole contemplation of the greatest good obtainable but only by the removal of uneasiness.*

---

* "Wherever there is uneasiness, there is desire . . . even in joy itself, that which keeps up the action whereon the enjoyment depends, is the desire to continue it, and the fear of losing it . . . ." The reader may remember Nietzsche's words: *"doch alle Lust will Ewigkeit . . . will tiefe, tiefe Ewigkeit."*

These remarks reflect the *sensualistic* as well as the *pessimistic* roots of psychoanalysis. The reader may not be prepared to discover these roots in the thought of the eighteenth century or in the intellectual atmosphere of the enlightenment known and once praised for its optimistic belief in man's progress and perfectibility, a belief which, in the eyes of one of its most powerful apologists, was not shaken by Rousseau's pathetic denunciations of man's misery and wretchedness.

We do not know whether Pinel was a student of the writings and the philosophy of Spinoza. We learned (25, II, p. 46) that after an initial disdainful rejection, a measure of acceptance of Spinoza's doctrine was reached towards the middle of the eighteenth century, i.e., during the formative years of Pinel, whose profound philosophical education and interest could hardly have bypassed one of the most controversial and contested figures and systems of his days, though the name of Spinoza does not occur in Pinel's writings.

In fact, "Towards the middle of the eighteenth century, exegetes of the Bible ceased to consider Spinoza as an atheist and saw him as the pantheist that he was. In an atmosphere which was becoming revolutionary, his ferment regained force and became active" (25, *ibid.*).

Spinoza distinguished four levels of knowledge, of which the lowest was opinion, which is knowledge subject to error.

At the level of "opinion" or "vague experience," according to Spinoza, only a more intense passion opposing the passion to which we are prey can liberate us from the latter. At the level of this conflict of the passions, therefore, one remains within the realm of the passions. No moral problem arises at this level, unless one considers the conflict of passions as a moral criterion aiming, if not at the annihilation of the passions, at least at their use as opposed to their free development. One is still at the level of *pure nature* in spite of the efforts made by many authors, ancient and modern, to detach a fragment of this nature to confer upon it the *name* of morality. It is this level which is faced by the physician who is studying passion as a purely natural phenomenon. Also, this is the point of departure chosen by Pinel, who restricted himself intentionally to the study of the passions in their purely natural stage, exempt from any moral stigma and admitting no moralistic reasoning. It is true that the *name* moral treatment has led to error, since most of its interpreters were unaware of the meaning of the French word *moral*, which often indicates only the antithesis to physical, a meaning assuredly adopted by Pinel in the term "moral treatment" which has become so famous.

Causal Thought in Pinel

The very fact that Pinel considered the human passions to be the true sources of mental alienation testifies to the *causal* nature of his view on mental alienation. But the passions were not the sole etiologic factors in insanity that were listed, described, and analyzed by the eminent alienist. In fact, there is hardly any sphere of human life which was neglected in his etiological thought. Thus he listed very vivid affections of the mind, such as ungovernable or disappointed ambition, religious fanaticism, profound chagrin, unfortunate love, domestic misfortunes, and imagination when unceasingly or ardently employed in certain professions. It was a sign of his highly developed critical sense that he saw *no necessary connection between the specific character of insanity, and the nature of its exciting cause.* The violence of maniacal paroxysms appeared to be independent of the nature of the exciting cause, or to depend, at least, much more upon the constitution of the individual and upon the different degrees of his physical and moral sensibility.

But Pinel's causal thought took its most surprising and unexpected direction when he raised the question whether maniacal paroxysms are the effects of a salutary reaction of the system. Here he referred to Stahl and his vitalistic interpretation of the organism in health and disease, and to Stahl's principle of conservation, whose office it is to repel any attack upon the system injurious to its well-being, or fatal to its existence. Evidently, it must have been the *vis medicatrix naturae* of the ancients which was on the minds of the seventeenth century Halle physician Stahl and his follower Pinel. But Pinel could not have been expected to anticipate similar views expressed in the second half of the nineteenth century by the eminent British neurologist, *Hughlings Jackson,* who distinguished among the effects of brain lesions those which betray their purely negative character from those which serve, though in an altered fashion, the maintenance of life and nervous function under the altered condition.

The conclusion, reached first by Aristotle and later by Bacon, that no more is needed for the *understanding* of a given phenomenon, event, or action than the knowledge of its determinants or causes, does not recommend itself to the searching mind impressed and captured by the wealth and shining diversity of these phenomena, events, or actions. Indeed, who wants to forego the splendor and the brilliancy emitted from the contacts, surprises, and persons surrounding every human existence, or who wants to leave out distress and misery from a biography? And still, not until we have brought all of these into the framework of our intellectual operations (or, in technical terms, transcendental logic), do we understand them. But then also, the splendor and brilliancy are gone and the enthusiastic mind deplores the decline of a sparkling and glittering world for which the barren and sober world of his understanding is no substitute. But such is man's situation that he must reach beyond the senses and elevate himself above their tempting luster to construct a world which he owes to himself alone and which affirms his greatness at every step, even though his greatness is embodied in abstractions, archetypes, and symbols rather than in concrete and perceptible objects and images. Should he give up this world of his own, he would fall an easy prey to the chaos of a structureless though perhaps shining chaos. Man, however, cannot escape from his greatness. *Non sit alterius qui suus esse potest.*

It is for this reason that the search for causes in the life sciences requires sobriety and self-denial. Here is no room for ecstasy, nor can we hope to facilitate this search by claiming identity, equality, or similarity of cause and effect.

The alarming questions as to whether organic diseases can be the effects of psychic causes and whether mental alienation may result from physical causes, have preoccupied the mind of the physician at all times. The first question might not have been a matter of great concern to Pinel. But the epistemological problem implied in this question cannot be isolated from the same problem implied in the second question. The problem has never been satisfactorily answered, nor has it ever been silenced. Remembering two of the first principles on which, in our view (45), causal investigations rest in the life sciences, i.e., the principle of the *multiciplicity* and that of the *individuality* of causes, we will forego at the onset any dogmatic solution. Similarly, we will dismiss any statistic solution, since the latter does not list nor even consider causal agents at work in a given individual; it is by its very nature and purpose a *collective* search. But in no branch of medical science is the *individual* structure of etiological constituents more obvious, its consideration more indispensable, its refined and detailed analysis more imperative than in nervous and mental diseases. But let us also remember that any causal relationship implies a *chronological* order of the events at stake, i.e., cause and effect (though the sequence is more than a simple *post hoc*; the effect is *necessitated* by its cause). To ascertain in a given case the causality of psychic phenomena, the latter must stand in an intelligible chronological relation to the effect; technically speaking, the distance or time interval between the effect, i.e., the disease, and its alleged cause, should not be too long. Finally, and most important, the psychical events believed to be causes of an organic disease must be proven to have displayed a symptom forming character in the past. Since, as a rule, psychical, and particularly emotional experiences, extend over a sizable fragment of an individual's biography, and since every organic disease or lesion has its own history, it is not an unfair demand to satisfy our need for a symptom forming character of the alleged psychical events demonstrable at some moment of the case history prior to the outbreak or definite appearance of the organic disease. *In a living being the parts are in a reciprocal and organogenic interrelation and interdependence. It is the disrupture of this interrelation which explains the genesis of symptoms emerging in this view as regional criteria and warning cries of a once perfect and now threatened integration.* Though this disrupture is a universal phenomenon, sparing no parts, it still makes itself felt in one organ with greater strength than in others, according to the greater affinity of the respective psychic factors to regional instrumentalities. This would account for the "choice" of an organ under the circumstances, some of the organs indeed being known as more or less selective scenes of action for corrsponding psychical agents, each of these actions having their organ-"physiognomy". Here, it is true, lingers the danger of outright speculation of a romantic and animistic interpretation of symptoms as mouth-pieces of an "eloquent" and meaningful nature. But man trying to decipher the language of nature is always exposed to the danger of doing so in terms of his own language. Thus originate those many ambiguities which are the dangerous outposts of human intelligence and the humiliating signs of man's limitations.

To be exact, no *object* can ever be made a cause. It is not objects but *changes* which obtain their position in the sequence of *events* by the cause-effect relationship. In primitive or magic thought, objects, though invisible and intangible, are still incriminated as causes of diseases. In a sense, the passage from primitive to rational medicine impresses the historian of medical ideas as that from a less to a more refined causal thought. It testifies to the astuteness of Hippocrates, the *philosopher* (legendary as he might be) so much admired by Pinel, the philosopher of mental alienation, that the "father of medicine" unmistakably recognized and adopted the refined causal thought in the few passages where he dealt with the problem. These passages are to be found in the genuine Hippocratic treatise, *On Airs,*

Waters, and Places. In a most general way, the author of the treatise
declares the importance of changes to reach far beyond their pathogenic effects. In fact, he stresses their formative role in the awakening of human intelligence: "It is changes of all kinds which arouse
the understanding of mankind, and do not allow them to get into
a torpid condition." More specifically, he dwells at length on the
changes of regimen and those of the seasons as causal factors of diseases. The latter were related to the great *epochs* of nature, thereby
assuming their time- and change-bound etiology. This view was revived by the renovator of Hippocratic medicine in the seventeenth
century, Thomas Sydenham. He revitalized the Hippocratic concept
of atmospheric constitutions which were believed to differ from year
to year and to ultimately result from unknown telluric causes which
he traced to unknown properties of the "bowels" of the earth.

Once the plurality of causes is recognized, there arises the rather
serious problem of knowing the way by which the different causal
agents, at times very numerous indeed, can be brought into that unity
of action which precedes the unity of reaction or effect displayed by
the disease of a given individual. In the past and present history of
medical thought, several terms have been used for this unification
of causes, such as composition, concurrence, and conjunction. In all
these and related terms the final product of this unification appears
to be the *compound* of several elements added together to build up
their sum total. But it is not too difficult to see the absurdity of a
procedure conceived on the model of arithmetic and destined to
bring into homogeneity and unity the most heterogeneous factors,
such as, e.g., a pathogenic agent, an idiosyncrasy, a seasonal, nutri-
tional or emotional constituent. Nor can the unified product be
visualized in perceptual or intuitive terms. It is neither the senses nor
the intuitive power which emerge as ultimate frames of reference
for man's effort to coordinate the various and numerous constituents
of a causal complex. The latter must be understood to be the result
of a spontaneous activity of man's understanding. In his search for
causes of diseases, far from being allowed to stay within the limits
of sensory experience, man is indebted to *thought* as to the foundation stone of one of the oldest and best explored branches of medicine, i.e., *etiology.*

This conclusion by no means implies the denial or undervalua-
tion of the sensory sources of medical experience. The conclusion is
only instrumental in assigning to these sources their places in the
whole of medical experience and in demarcating them from the conceptual sources of this experience. There is more *thought* in the

latter than we are taught and inclined to ascribe to a segment of human knowledge which, since the days of antiquity and Hippocratic medicine, rests on observation of sensory data. Nobody doubts the logical (or, still better the transcendental-logical) structure of the relation which human understanding establishes between cause and effect. But we must learn that the causes themselves, when acting in common, cannot deny their conceptual frame holding together the sensual constituents as their raw material, which human understanding uses for the construction of etiological thought. It seems that natural data cannot reach us unless they are screened and shaped by the activity and spontaneity of human understanding. Diseases are no exception to this rule; they too are subject to the first principles of natural science. This long argument finally leads to a better understanding of *Pinel's* repeatedly stated *definition of disease as a compound idea.*

A System of the Art of Thinking According to Condillac

"Q" Now, one has no proper conception of a thing until one is in a position to make an analysis of it. Do you wish, for example, to conceive of a machine? Take it apart, taking careful note of the relations between all its parts; and, as you separate them, take care to arrange them in an order which will prevent any confusion. If afterwards you reassemble them, observing how they act upon each other, you will understand the origin of the whole machine and you will conceive it perfectly. This is what must be done with all ideas which are to compose a system.

This is all the more necessary because most of our ideas are for us what machines are for those who have no knowledge of statics. They have settled into our minds ready-made, just as circumstances or those who have watched over our education have transmitted them to us. If sometimes we have formed them ourselves, it has been with so little reflection that, since we have not noticed the order we have followed, they offer merely something vague. Often they are only words, to which we would have great difficulty in attaching a significance.

We shall not surmount these obstacles unless we are very clearly aware of all that we include in the notions that we have formed.

"Q" It is necessary to note all their partial ideas, consider each one
separately, combine them in different relations, and finally put
them into the order in which they retain the highest degree of
association. Then we shall grasp them easily and clearly and
shall understand their origin entirely.

What we have done for some notions, we must do for all areas
of the art which we wish to reduce to a system. In this way they
will be so well-developed that we shall see them all arising from
one primary idea.

If you wish, therefore, to know whether you are in a position to
construct a system, try to decompose it into all the constituent
parts. If you cannot do so, because there are some of which you
have only a vague notion or which are totally unknown to you,
abandon the undertaking.

If I wish, for example, to construct a system on the art of
thinking, I consider human understanding as a faculty which
receives ideas, and which makes them the subject of its operations. But I readily note that the notions of faculty, idea, and
operation are abstractions. Consequently, none of them is the
first principle which I am seeking. I therefore decompose further and review all the operations. Conception presents itself
first as the most perfect, but I conceive only because I judge or
because I reason; I form judgments and reasonings only because
I compare; I should not be able to compare, in all the relations
in which I need to do so, if I did not distinguish, compose, decompose, and form abstractions. All this necessarily demands
that I be capable of reflecting. Reflection presupposes imagination or memory and these two operations are obviously the
effect of attention, which cannot take place without perception.
Finally, perception comes with sensations, and it is merely the
impression that each sense object makes upon me.

This decomposition thus leads me to an idea which is by no
means abstract, and it indicates to me that perception is the
germ of all the operations of understanding. In fact, the exercise of this faculty can be nothing less than perceiving (aperce-
voir); it can begin neither sooner nor later. It is, therefore,
perception which must become successively attention, imagination, memory, reflection and, finally, understanding itself. But
I shall not achieve this progress at all if I do not have a very
clear idea of each operation; on the contrary, I should become

"Q" confused and fall into misapprehensions. This, I must confess, is what happened to me when I was discussing the origin of human knowledge. I did not know the precepts which I advance today well enough to follow them exactly. You must not expect me to correct in this chapter the errors of that work. . . .

The method that I use to construct these systems I call analysis. We know that it comprises two operations, decomposition and composition.

By the first, one separates all the ideas which belong to a subject, and one examines them until one has discovered the idea which must be the germ of all the others. By the second, one arranges them according to the order of their generation. But the less exactly one has performed the decomposition, the further one will be from grasping their true generation. . . .

In algebraic analysis, the mind is working solely upon signs; this is why obscurity increases as one becomes engaged in a longer succession of calculations. This method is, nevertheless, very helpful. Without it the mind would often be held back and perhaps sometimes brought to a complete standstill by the necessity for concentrating the attention upon too great a number of objects. By expressing a great many ideas in a few signs, it facilitates the passage from one truth to another; and if it produces some obscurity, it is only temporarily; no sooner has one arrived at the intended objective, than light is shed upon the whole way that one has traveled.

When algebraic analysis does not enlighten the mind, it is not, then, because it lacks by nature all that is needed for enlightening; it is because the algebraist sacrifices to facility and rapidity of operations an insight which he is always sure of obtaining. I speak here on the authority of the mathematicians themselves.

This method is, therefore, the sole principle of all discoveries made in mathematics. In fact, if one opens the works of the modern geometers who have made the greatest use of synthesis and who have praised it most highly, one easily recognizes analysis in disguise. But would these great men not have done more for the advancement of sciences by revealing their secret themselves instead of having us follow them while hiding from us the path over which they were leading us.

Metaphysical analysis has the advantage of never ceasing to

"Q" enlighten the mind, because it makes the mind work continuously upon ideas and forces it to follow their generation in a manner so obvious that it would be impossible to lose sight of it. Thus it discovers no truths which it cannot demonstrate. The metaphysician is all the more blameworthy for having recourse to synthesis in that his ideas are naturally vague and only analysis can give them precision and preserve it for them. The geometer is more excusable because, since ideas of quantity are in themselves perfectly well-defined, analysis is not as necessary to his demonstrations. If he must give it preference, it is less for greater exactness than in order to be more within the reach of the reader and to teach him the art of making discoveries.

I shall not dwell upon further demonstration of the way in which metaphysical analysis differs from algebraic analysis. I think that I have conveyed my idea of the first, and the second is known from the works of the geometers. It is enough for me to have proved that one must follow no other method, whether one aspires to new knowledge or wishes to demonstrate some truth.

It is especially the province of metaphysical analysis to establish the true system of each art. It alone can show the formulation of rules, reduce them to the smallest number possible, and render more useful the theory of arts.

It may be that this method will be deemed impracticable in situations where there is merely a question of surmounting difficulties. It is rarely that one can encompass in one glance all the branches of an art, link them together, and bring them into a system. That is what characterizes the man of genius. Those who see only one side of things and fail to grasp their different relations, may have great talents, but they are merely second-rate men. As for the philosophers who claim to owe a great deal to abstract principles and to gratuitous suppositions, we have said enough about them (16, *Traité des systèmes.* Chap. 17).

Now, if we reflect upon the manner in which we acquire knowledge by sight, we shall notice that a very diversified object, such as a vast landscape, is somewhat broken up, since we know it only when its parts have come to arrange themselves one after the other in orderly fashion in the mind.

We have seen in what order this decomposition proceeds. The principal objects are the first to place themselves in the mind;

"Q" the others come afterwards and arrange themselves according to their relation with the first. We perform this decomposition only because an instant is not sufficient for studying all these objects. But we decompose only to recompose, and once the knowledge has been acquired, the things, instead of being successive, have in the mind the same simultaneous order that they have outside. It is in this simultaneous order that our knowledge of them consists; for, if we could not visualize them together, we should never be able to judge them in relation to each other and we should know them poorly.

To analyze is, then, nothing more than to observe in successive order the qualities of an object in order to give them in the mind the simultaneous order in which they exist. This is what nature makes all of us do. Analysis which is thought to be known only to the philosophers is, therefore, known to everyone, and I have taught the reader nothing; I have only made him notice what he does continually.

Though I distinguish at a glance a multitude of objects in a landscape that I have studied, nevertheless the sight is never more distinct than when it restricts itself, and I look at only a few objects at a time: we always discern less than we see.

It is the same with the mind's view. I have present at one time many fragments of knowledge which have become familiar to me; I see all of them but I do not discern them all equally. In order to see in a distinct manner all that offers itself at one time to my mind, I must decompose as I decomposed what offered itself to my eyes: I must analyze my thought.

This analysis is performed in a way no different from that of outer objects. One decomposes in the same way: one retraces the constituents of one's thought in successive order in order to reestablish them in simultaneous order: one performs this composition and decomposition in conformity with the relations that exist among the things, as principal and subordinate; and, since one would not analyze a landscape if sight did not entirely encompass it, so one would not analyze one's thought if the mind did not encompass it entirely. In both cases, it is necessary to see everything at one time; otherwise one could not be sure of having seen all the constituents one after the other (16, *La Logique*, part I, Ch. 2).

"Q" Each of us can notice that he knows perceptible objects only by the sensations that he receives from them; it is the sensations which represent them for us.

If we are sure that, when they are present, we see them only in the sensations that they produce upon us at the moment, we are no less sure that, when they are absent, we see them only in the memory of the sensations which they have produced. All the knowledge that we can have of perceptible objects is, therefore, in principle, and can only be, sensations.

Sensations, considered as representations of perceptible objects, are called *ideas*, a figurative expression which properly means the same thing as *images*.

The more different sensations we distinguish, the more sorts of ideas we distinguish; and these ideas are either actual sensations or merely the memory of sensations that we have had.

When we acquire them by the analytical method discovered in the preceding chapter, they arrange themselves in orderly fashion in the mind: they preserve there the order that we have given them, and we can easily retrace them with the same clearness with which we have acquired them. If, instead of acquiring them by this method, we accumulate them at random, they will be in great confusion, and will remain so. This confusion will not allow the mind to recall them distinctly, and if we wish to speak of knowledge that we think we have acquired, what we are saying will be incomprehensible because we will not understand it ourselves. In order to speak in an understandable manner, it is necessary to conceive and transmit one's ideas in analytical order, which decomposes and recomposes each thought. This order is the only one which can give them all the clarity and all the precision of which they are capable, and, since we have no other way of instructing ourselves, we have no other for communicating our knowledge. I have already proved it, but I come back to it and I shall come back to it again; for this truth is not sufficiently known. It is even contested, though it is simple, obvious, and fundamental.

In fact, should I wish to understand a machine, I would take it apart in order to study each part separately. When I have an exact idea of each one and can put them back in the same order in which they were, then I shall understand this machine to per-

"Q" fection, because I have decomposed it and recomposed it.

What is it, then, to understand this machine? It is to have a thought which is composed of as many ideas as there are parts in this machine itself, ideas which represent each one exactly and which are arranged in the same order.

When I have studied it according to this method, which is the only one, then my thought will comprise only distinct ideas; and it analyzes itself, whether I wish to be aware of it myself or make others aware of it. . . . There are sound minds which seem never to have studied because they do not seem to have applied themselves intentionally to learning; however, they have studied and they have done it well. Since they did it without premeditated design, it did not occur to them that they were taking lessons from a teacher, yet they had the best of all—nature. It was she who made them analyze the things they studied; and the little that they do know, they know well. Instinct, which is such a sure guide; taste, which judges so well, and yet judges at the very moment it senses; talent, which is itself merely taste, when it produces what it judges: all these faculties are the work of nature, which by causing us to analyze unknowingly, seems to wish to hide from us how much we owe to her. It is she who inspires the man of genius; she is the muse that he invokes when he does not know whence his thoughts come (16, *La Logique*, part I, Ch. 3).

. . . Now, if we observe the order and the genesis of ideas, we shall see them arise successively one from the other; and if this succession conforms to the manner in which we acquire them, we shall have analyzed them well. The order of analysis, therefore, is in this case the same as the order of the genesis of ideas. We have said that the ideas of perceptible objects are, in their origin, merely the sensations which represent these objects. But in nature only individuals exist; hence our first ideas are only individual ideas, ideas of such and such an object.

We have not devised names for each individual; we have only grouped individuals into different classes, which we distinguish by special names; and these classes are what we call *genera* and *species*. We have, for example, put into the class of *trees* plants whose stems rise to a certain height to divide into a multitude of branches which form a more or less thick cluster. This is a general class that we call *genus*. When subsequently it was ob-

"Q" served that trees differ in size, structure, fruit, etc., other classes were distinguished which are subordinate to the first, which includes them all; these subordinate classes are what we call *species.*

It is thus that we group into different classes everything that comes to our knowledge; by this means we assign to each one a well-defined place and we always know where to find them. Let us forget these classes for a moment and imagine that a different name has been given to each individual; we realize at once that the mulitude of names would have fatigued our memory so as to confuse everything and that it would have been impossible for us to study the objects which multiplied before our eyes and form distinct ideas of them.

Nothing is, therefore, more reasonable than this distribution; and when we consider how useful, or even necessary, it is to us, we might be inclined to believe that we did it on purpose. But we would be mistaken; this purpose belongs to nature alone; it is she who began it unknown to us.

A child will call *tree*, as we tell him, the first tree that we show him, and this name will be for him the name of an individual. However, if he is shown another tree, he will not think of asking for its name; he will call it *tree* and will give this common name to two individuals. He will give it in the same way to three or four and finally to all the plants which will seem to bear some resemblance to the first tree he saw. This name will even become so general that he will call *tree* everything that we call *plant.* He is naturally inclined to generalize because it is more convenient for him to use a word he knows than learn a new one. He generalizes, then, without intending to generalize and without even noticing that he is generalizing. In this way an individual idea suddenly becomes general; often it even becomes too much so, and this happens whenever we confuse things it would have been useful to distinguish.

This child will soon realize it himself. He will not say, *"I have generalized too much; I must distinguish different species of trees";* he will form, unintentionally and without being aware of it, subordinate classes, just as he formed, unintentionally and without being aware of it, general classes. He will do no more than follow his needs. This is why I say that he will make these groupings unintentionally and without being aware of it. In

"Q" fact, if he is taken into a garden, and is made to pick and eat different sorts of fruit, we shall see that he will soon learn the names cherry tree, peach tree, pear tree, and apple tree and that he will distinguish the different species of trees (16, *La Logique*, part I, Ch. 4).

Pinel on Analytical Method — I

The general way of the human intellect in its investigations should always be to proceed from the simple to the complex, to consider, by means of analysis, the least complicated objects first and then to advance to the others by a sort of wisely conducted progression; there is no other secret at all for attaining clear and precise ideas of diseases. One should train oneself first in hospitals or asylums to grasp well the distinctive characteristics of what I call *simple species*, examples of which I give later. . . . I compile for example, two distinct series of symptoms, one group properly related to a disorder of the respiratory tract, the other to one of the alimentary canal. I consider separately their various degrees of intensity, their courses, their respective predominance, their danger; I state the complicated nature of the disease, and, determining the general principles of treatment, I modify the latter in accordance with additional considerations based upon the age, the sex, the way of living, and the particular constitution of the patient (1a, p. 9).

Pinel on Analytical Method — II

As a tool, the analytical method occupies the foreground in Pinel's work. Moreover, he has defined it in each of his three great works, each definition differing from the others. The definition of it which he gives in the introduction to the first (1798) and second (1804) editions of his *Nosographie philosophique* (2) (which has as its significant subtitle *La Méthode de l'analyse appliquée à la médecine*) is not distinguishable from the authentic formula of *Condillac*, which the illustrious alienist repeats verbatim:

"To analyze," says Condillac, "is merely to observe in successive order the characteristics of an object in order to give them in the mind the simultaneous order in which they exist. . . . Now, what is this order? Nature herself indicates it; it is the one in which she offers objects: there are some which especially attract the attention; they are more striking, they dominate, and all the others seem to arrange themselves around them and by them" (2, p. XII) .

This definition is preceded by a most significant historical remark, in which the author acclaims Hippocrates as the first physician to adopt the analytical method:

How can one fail to admire the analytical method adopted by the father of medicine as the only true and unchanging one in the search for truth—his profound wisdom in showing, by a chronological exposition of facts, the course of nature left to herself in acute diseases; his pains in extending his viewpoint afterwards to the medical constitution of the seasons; and, finally, his care to generalize his views and compose aphorisms, doubtless sometimes liable to exceptions, but always abundant in great truths and more often than not confirmed by enlightened observation?

Has not all sound progress made by medicine in every age been due to the same analytical method, and what may we not expect from its application to the whole doctrine and the public teaching of this science?

The first edition of the *Traité médico-philosophique sur l'aliénation mentale* appeared in 1801, the second in 1809. We read in the chapter entitled "General Design of the Work":

I abide strictly by observation, which teaches what it would have been difficult even to suspect, namely, that there can be a separate disorder in the ideas received from external impressions, in the memory, the imagination, the judgment, the awareness of one's own existence, the impulse of the will; and that these disorders, combined in greater or lesser number and with different degrees of intensity, form an infinite number of variations. It is all the more necessary to emphasize these fundamental subjects and to recommend, above all, the special study of them if one wishes to proceed in more orderly fashion in the observation of the phenomena of alienation, to apply the analytical method more successfully to this disease, and to cause new progress to be made in its general history (3, p. 5).

The following paragraph contains the *definition of the analytical method as it is applied by Pinel to the study of mental alienation*:

. . . with continuous attention to and thorough study of the symptoms which are peculiar to them, one can classify them in a general way, and distinguish between them as fundamental disturbances of the understanding or of the will, leaving aside the considerations of their innumerable variations. A more or less marked delirium on almost every subject is associated, in some insane persons, with a state of agitation and fury; this properly constitutes *mania*. The delirium may be selective and restricted to a particular series of subjects, with a sort of stupor and intense and profound emotions: this is what is called *melancholia*. Sometimes a general weakness attacks the intellectual and affective functions, as in old age, and produces what is called *dementia*. Finally, the obliteration of reason, with rapid and automatic outbursts of rage, is designated as idiocy. These are the four types of aberration which are indicated in a general way by the term mental alienation (52).

In short, the analytical method demands *observation* as its primary constituent. By means of this method one may arrive at a *classification* of the different forms of mental alienation, a classification established by Pinel according to fundamental disturbances of the understanding or of the will. It is not difficult to recognize in this principle of classification the *heritage from Locke and Condillac, but especially from Bacon* and the *Encyclopédie* (1751-1777), in which the system of *Human Knowledge* is established according to the model of classification based by Bacon upon the three faculties of the mind: memory, imagination, and reason.

The third source of our knowledge of the analytical method as defined and applied to medicine by Pinel is provided by his work entitled *La médecine clinique rendue plus précise et plus exacte par l'application de l'analyse,* the first edition of which appeared in 1802, the second in 1804. The object of this new approach to clinical medicine was:

. . . to make a felicitous application of the luminous precept given by Condillac in his *Logic*: To discern upon this immense horizon extensive points of view; to consider them separately with the most scrupulous attention; to coordinate them and produce from them a vast whole (16, *La Logique*, p. 2).

Again, the sensualistic heritage from Locke and Condillac is implied in the question raised by Pinel when he is seeking some means to escape from the blind alley into which the vain clinical investigations of the centuries preceding him had led (here he again quotes Condillac) :

The internal mechanism of the organic functions, the reciprocal action of fluids and solids in the living body, should not these inexhaustible subjects of futile reasoning, of trivial discussions and explanations, be henceforth banished from clinical medicine as they are from the other areas of natural history, and should we not limit ourselves to perceptible phenomena, that is, to impressions received by sight, touch, smell, hearing? Have we any other means of recognizing internal disorders than by external signs and the results of previous investigations upon analogous subjects? Moreover, it is by paying close attention to each of these signs and to their varying degrees of intensity, to the danger, great or small, that they may entail, or the hope they should inspire, that one can judge sanely. But these are still merely isolated and disconnected ideas if one does not, as it were, disregard everything which does not belong to the essential nature of the disease, if one does not bring together its distinctive features and if one does not grasp its salient points of similarity to other diseases described by the authors or observed by oneself (16, *La Logique*, p. 23).

Let us add to these three sources of our knowledge of analysis as applied to medicine by Pinel, the still less-known article on the same subject which he wrote for the *Dictionnaire des Sciences Médicales* (1). He reaffirms the nature and aim of the method designed to guarantee the exactness of descriptions and the manner of *characterizing diseases by external signs, excluding all conjectural opinion, in order to attain finally a simple and natural classification of them. Time and time again Pinel refers to the method used by the natural sciences as his model.* From the beginning of his career, he has stressed the linking of clinical medicine with all the physical sciences and their methods. In other words, *it is the natural history of diseases which he is seeking to learn and to write about*. So, in the dictionary article of 1812, he considers it necessary to take pains to describe acute diseases in the hospitals, day by day, from the moment of their onset to their complete termination, in order to be able afterwards to make exact comparisons between them and in this way to grasp their affinities or their specific differences. It is essential also not to confuse basic symptoms with those pertaining to differences of age, climate, seasons, and so on. The informed reader will recognize in this the Hippocratic heritage which was acknowledged repeatedly and almost solemnly by Pinel. *The history of the passions, too, is a part of the natural history of the disease, that is, of mental alienation.* The passions must be considered *"without regard to morality* and only as *simple phenomena of human life"* (3, p. XII) . The reader who grasps the spirit and the letter of this thesis, which expresses admirably the philosophical attitude of Pinel, is safe from an erroneous interpretation of *moral treatment;* the latter is no exception to the *natural* therapeutic measures applied to all diseases since the time of the father of medicine.

The 1812 dictionary article also contains an autobiographical fragment on Pinel and his career. Though it was written about ten years after the publication of the *Traité médico-philosophique sur l'aliénation mentale,* no mention is made in this article of that treatise, while Pinel proudly cites the three editions of his *Nosographie.* In fact, it is as a *clinician* that Pinel reaffirms himself in this article. One ventures to believe that the illustrious alienist would have refused the designation of specialist in the sense imposed upon that word by the division of labor and by qualifications so significant in contemporary medicine. *It was surely not without reason and profound conviction that Pinel included the term "philosophique" in his Traité médico-philosophique sur l'aliénation mentale.*

In the century which shaped Pinel's mind, a philosopher was defined as "one who devotes himself to the study of the sciences and who seeks to know effects by their causes and by their principles" (21a) . According to Paul Hazard (25, p. 371) , taking his inspiration from the *Encyclopédie,* the philosophical spirit of the eighteenth century was "a spirit of observation and of precision, which refers everything to its true principles." These statements remove all doubt that Pinel, a faithful observer and learned interpreter of vital phenomena, chose the term *philosophique* in full awareness of the usage and the spirit of the eighteenth century.

Pinel on Applied Analytical Method

The sameness of the principle of classification* should protect human knowledge from decomposition and loss of its wholeness. It was not without reason that Bacon repeatedly insisted on the individual as the proper and sole target of observation and examination, warning against abstractions and so-called systems of thought, thereby re-affirming and, in a sense, justifying the title of the first representative of an experimental philosophy. Thus, when, in our own days, classifications proved to be detrimental to individual research and to the wholeness of human intellect and experience, this occurred because of a disregard for those cautions and reserves which the pioneers of classifications themselves erected as barriers to abuse. More than once, this writer had the experience that one has to go back to the origins and first enunciations of principles and doctrines, above all in those cases in which distortions and arbitrary interpretations finally discredit their first and authentic explorer, who, often enough, has the touch of a genius rather than that of a not altogether impartial though fervent apologist.

We saw that in Pinel's medical thought the analytical method ultimately culminated in classification (53) ; thus, one cannot expect definitions of the two terms to be basically different. In fact, the analytic method adopted by Pinel, in conformity with the teaching of Condillac, implied the mental process of tracing compound diseases to their elements or simple diseases. Symptoms must be observed carefully, with no preconceived idea. In his attempt (2a) to delimit by his abstracting power the specific characters of a given disease, the physician is assisted by previous observations of his own and those made by others. Then the disease will be identified as to species and name, and, finally, individual variations will be determined. Pinel's *applied analytic method* comprises:

(1) The investigation of symptoms, made regardless of any hypothesis, and solely by the senses. Careful examination is made of the patient's previous physical and mental condition; this is sometimes most difficult indeed, due to concerted fabrications or conscious reserve.

---

* Pinel's views on classification will be treated again in one of the following chapters. In view of the relation of classification to the analytical method, repetition of the same subject could not be avoided.

(2) Disregarding, at first, by a sort of abstraction, individual variations, one should pay attention only to the distinctive and specific characters of a given disease which, incidentally, one ought to know by one's own observation or that of others. Sharp differentiation should be made between the various types of symptoms which, combined, constitute a compound disease, but isolated, must be related to different diseases.

(3) This is succeeded by the differentiation of the species, name, and nosographic place of a given disease. To reach a well-founded conclusion, it may be necessary to follow up its course for several days; particularly in obscure cases, utmost precaution and reticence are needed to prevent premature and unfounded judgment.

(4) Finally, attention must be given to the individual factors of age, sex, way of life, and habits which may influence the course of the disease and modify its type. Last but not least, the evolutionary stages of diseases or their natural history must be included in this general march of the human intellect, in which Pinel distinguished the three constituents of the classifying physician: *sensibility, memory,* and *judgment.*

Pinel's repeated advice to go back to primary diseases as the constituents of compound ones no longer seems to be of actual importance. The clinician, particularly the neurologist, trained in the scientific thought of our time, has learned to question the very existence of elementary activities and to conceive of each of them as the result of the integrated activity of all of them. He would consider the difference between compound and simple diseases as merely relative. The case is different, however, with another criterion of Pinel's analytic method, one that allows diseases to be classified according to symptoms and to regions involved in lesions; obviously this was a combined principle of classification that stood the test of time (38). In brief, the use of the analytic method implied faithful and repeated observations; it promised controlled diagnosis and classification.

It was by reasoning similar to the analytic method that, in the nineteenth century, the experimental physiologist and therapist turned to elementary mechanisms as the true constituents of disease. It was a logical and further step in the same direction when Claude Bernard, in his posthumous work, denounced classifications as irrelevant and not in harmony with the true purpose of experimental medicine, which is solely interested in the investigation of the proximate causes (that is, in the analysis and interpretation), but not in

the labelling and grouping of natural phenomena. Why did Pinel
not make the same step, why did he allow his analytic method to
come to its end when facing the idea of a species believed to be a
simple or elementary disease? Since he conceived the species as a kind
of compound idea (*une sorte d'idée complexe*), the door was actually open to its final decomposition. Should Pinel have made the
step, he would indeed have ceased to be a nosographer. That, in
fact, he refrained from bringing his method to its logical end at a
time, it is true, when the experimental method was not clearly defined as yet, can be explained only by Pinel's concept of science. As
a faithful pupil of the ancients, he saw the criterion of science in
generalization. He must have experienced the fateful passage, made
by himself at the bedside, from generalization to individualization
as the passage from science to life or from thought to action; this
assumption is borne out by his remark (2a) that the consideration
and evaluation of the individual features of diseases, while indispensable for an intelligent treatment, are only disturbing in the
general history of diseases, intended to be a subject of teaching.

A given disease may be modified by locality, climate, reason, profession, age, temperament, way of life, previous or chronic diseases,
and so forth. This constitutes another body of considerations, needed
indeed for an intelligent guidance of the patient under given circumstances. But, as a rule, case histories intended to serve as teaching
material or as models of a general history of disease or epidemics,
should not be overburdened with individual details.

It took another century to realize that the criterion of science
cannot be denied to an individual fact (45), provided it becomes
integrated into a *totality* of facts or a *system* of knowledge alone
deserving and conveying the criterion of science.

When attempting to classify the "varieties of insanity," Pinel
adopted the basic faculties of the mind as a principle of classification.

"Q" In some instances of mental derangement, all the powers of the
mind are either absolutely enfeebled or more than usually
excited. In other instances, the change or perversion affects but
one or a few of the intellectual faculties, while the others are
found to acquire a new degree of development and activity. It
is not uncommon to see maniacs absorbed by one idea exclusively. Thus occupied, they remain motionless and silent in a
corner of their apartment, repel with rudeness the services that
are offered to them, and betray, in all their features, the marks
of a fixed stupidity. Others, during their paroxysms, are inces-

santly agitated—they laugh, cry and sing by turns, discover a most versatile mobility, and are not able to fix their attention for a single moment (4, pp. 22-23) .

There can hardly be any doubt that Pinel, in his attempt to classify the varieties of insanity according to the sources of human knowledge or the faculties of the mind, was under the influence of Diderot and D'Alembert and the *"discours préliminaire"* of their *Dictionnaire raisonné des Sciences, des Arts et des Métiers.* That, generally speaking, Pinel was close to the Encyclopedists, can already be inferred from his friendship with Condorcet, who was induced by d'Alembert to take an active part in the preparation of the *Encyclopédie.*

Pinel Adopts the Method Used in Natural Science

"Q" It is with intention that I have chosen the subject that is most obscure and the most exposed to endless divagations (if one allows onself to be swayed by speculation) , and what subject would appear more marvelous and more difficult to conceive than the nature of the functions of the human understanding, their gradual development, their different degrees of power, their changes as a result of physical impressions, and the aberrations which they may suffer? It is still more difficult to go back to the origin of the various isolated or combined lesions which may affect the perception of external objects, memory, imagination, judgment, or the feeling of one's own existence; and can one observe the slightest relation between these various lesions and the structure of the organ which seems to be their seat? One should, therefore, have in view a more stable goal and follow a surer course, namely, to confine onself strictly to the observation of facts and to achieve a general and well-defined history of mental alienation; this can result only from the bringing together of a great many individual observations, made with great care during the course and the various periods of the disease from its beginning to its end. But, for these examples to become materials suitable for use, is it not necessary that the symptoms and distinctive signs whose nature and succession in these particular cases one wishes to trace be studied first in a

"Q" large hospital, and that a severe critic learn to reject all those
which are ambiguous or doubtful and admit only those which
are obvious, which leave no room for vague reasonings, and
which have been observed the most constantly in different types
of mental aberration? The true foundation of the whole edi-
fice is, therefore, a preliminary and thorough study of the
various disorders of the understanding and the will manifested
externally by changes in bodily posture, by gestures and words
likely to express the inner state and by unmistakable physical
disturbances (3, p. 3).

On Gay or Expansive Passions Considered
Likely to Derange the Mind

"Q" Painters and sculptors have portrayed truly and forcefully the
distinctive characteristics of these passions, marked outwardly
by a sort of brightening up of the face and the simultaneous
contraction of certain muscles. I should speak here only of those
which, through their extreme intensity, are likely to derange
the mind: joy, pride, love, or ecstatic rapture or admiration concentrated upon religious objects. The affections, similarly, when
left within certain bounds, seem to stimulate the understanding
to function with greater vivacity and animation; but raised to
the highest degree or exacerbated by obstacles, they produce
nothing more than violent aberrations, a temporary delirium,
a state of stupor, or manifest insanity.

Very intense joy and unexpected prosperity may profoundly
shock weak minds and lead to mental aberration; but is it not
rather the result of successive shocks of the opposite nature produced by intense frustration or profound sorrows? (As an
example Pinel notes the case history reported in his *Traité*, pp.
34-35.)

Hope, which is merely anticipated joy produced by the thought
of good to come, is likely to produce heights of fancy and exercise the most powerful temptation, especially when directed
toward objects of vanity or pride; the result is an exalted self-
esteem and a profound conviction of being worthy of high position, especially in youth or the prime of life. Thus unexpected
reverses or adverse circumstances produce intense shocks and

"Q" may lead to manifest insanity. Examples of this are by no means rare in the private institutions devoted to the treatment of this disease.

It is common to find mental alienation accompanied by a haughty manner and inflated pride which occurs only during the attack and as a characteristic symptom of it. This same vice displayed from youth onward in high degree and as if inherent in the constitution, grows greater and greater, reaches a peak, and becomes the cause of real mania. A tall, middle-aged man attracted attention by the harshness of his expressions and answers as well as by his violent transports and austere habits. His bearing and his facial expression bore the imprint of haughtiness and of the most easily offended and morose nature. He was continually apprehensive and uttered bitter reproaches against those around him. His savage misanthropy was increased still further by business reverses, and it was then that insanity became manifest. He issued bills of exchange for exorbitant sums on his banker as well as on other firms with which he had no connection, and soon afterwards he was committed for insanity. He preserved the same haughtiness in the place of detention, and he gave orders with all the arrogance of an Asiatic despot; he eventually thought that he was chancellor of England, Duke of Batavia, and a powerful monarch. (Dr. Perfect, *Annals of Insanity*).

There are often admitted to the mental hospitals young persons of 18 to 22 years of age who have become deranged because of obstacles encountered to an imminent marriage. There was sometimes violent, frenzied delirium; at other times the gloomiest melancholy. It is not unusual to see manifested a state of stupor and a kind of idiocy; at certain times also the intervals of insanity are periodic and are separated by lucid intervals. Extreme purity of sentiment may characterize the first transports of love and give rise to mental aberration.

A young working girl had fallen hopelessly in love with a man whom she often saw pass her window, but with whom she had never spoken. The image of the beloved object alone occupied her thoughts during her insanity, and she displayed such antipathy for other men that she struck her companions in misfortune when they were strong and of masculine appearance, believing them to be men in disguise. Another young woman

"Q" whose marriage was imminent became so offended, or rather outraged, by proposals of anticipated favors made by her fiancé, and was so deeply distressed by it that her mind became deranged (3, pp. 34-37).*

Spasmodic Passions Likely to Cause Alienation

"Q" Passions, generally speaking, are unknown modifications of physical and psychical sensibility whose distinctive characteristics we can disentangle and establish only by external signs. However contradictory some of them, such as anger, fear, intense pain, or sudden joy, may seem, they are marked especially by various spasms of the facial muscles and by striking expressions, of which the most eminent poets, sculptors, and painters have made the most profound study. The trained eye of the anatomist can ascertain the muscles which, by their separate, simultaneous or successive actions, serve to express the passions of which I speak as well as all those which can move us.

The nature of the object which excites the anger, the contributory ideas which attach themselves to it, the association of some other passion, and the degree of individual sensibility can produce very different expressions of this passion. But when it is simple, artists and true observers are agreed in attributing to it the following signs: a red and inflamed face or else a ghastly pallor, wild and flashing eyes, raised eyebrows, furrowed forehead, lips pressed together, especially in the center, a sort of indignant and disdainful laughter, clenching of the jaws, sometimes with grinding of the teeth, and swelling of the veins of the neck and the temples.

---

* I cannot recall without very painful sentiments the case of a beautiful young woman, brought to the hospital in a state of the most violent delirium, after having been abandoned in cowardly fashion by her lover during the ninth month of pregnancy. Three months afterwards her fury calmed down and was followed by a gloomy stupor and an irresistible impulse to suicide. One morning she shrewdly tied a shoe-lace around her neck and hid in her bed to escape the watchfulness of the guard. She was almost suffocated, and it was only by assiduous and prolonged care that she was restored to life. As soon as she was revived, she gazed fiercely at those who had helped her and reproached them menacingly for the hateful service of having prolonged her deplorable existence. (Pinel's footnote).

"Q" Repeated transports of anger are always detrimental to judgment, preventing its free exercise, and an extreme irascibility is sometimes the premonitory sign of alienation or a strong predisposition toward incurring it. It is to be feared in women especially during the menses or following childbirth, as proved by frequent examples which I have noticed at the Salpêtrière. If it becomes a habit, it may lead, in melancholics, to a furious delirium or a state of stupor or dementia. A woman who was very active, and admirable moreover for her domestic virtues, had for a long time been indulging in unrestrained and unreserved anger for the slightest reasons. A simple incident, a slight delay in the execution of her orders, the smallest fault of her servants or children, were followed by a violent transport or a tumultuous scene. This unfortunate tendency reached its limit, and a complete mental alienation resulted.

A feeling of horror or intense fear and the ultimate degree of despair, though one could hardly consider them synonymous, have a great similarity in the spasms of the facial muscles they produce: brow completely burrowed, lowering of the eyebrows, contracted pupils, eyes flashing and restless, nostrils wide open and raised. The disturbance can sometimes be so profound that the reason is deranged thereby. There were received into the hospital, at different times but within a short interval, three young women who had become insane, one by the sight of a supposed phantom dressed in white which had been shown to her during the night by some young people, another by a violent clap of thunder at a certain time of the month, and the third by the horror inspired by an evil place where she had been taken by trickery (3, pp. 25-27).

On Weakening or Depressing Passions

These passions, such as grief, hate, fear, regret, remorse, jealousy, and envy, which are the source of so many disorders and ills in social life, have also served to enrich the fine arts and are vividly portrayed in some of the masterpieces by painters and sculptors of the first order. They are capable of varying degrees of power and of infinite nuances, depending on their conjunction with some other passion, individual sensibility, the contributory ideas

"Q" which go along with them, or the force of the determining cause. But they degenerate into mental alienation only when they have reached a very high degree of intensity, when there is abrupt transition from one to the other or the shock of their reversal. The external signs of a profound sorrow are generally a feeling of languor, a great decrease of muscular strength, loss of appetite, facial pallor, a feeling of fullness and oppression, labored breathing sometimes interrupted by sobs, a more or less profound torpor, and finally a dismal stupor or the most violent delirium.

It will always be praiseworthy to remain true to one's character and to preserve one's equanimity in prosperity and adversity alike; but this counsel of wisdom, so often embellished with poetic charm, gains new weight in the consideration of the physical ills, mental aberration especially, which can result from disregarding it. This is not the only example of the support which medicine lends to morale. Melancholics are especially prone to carry to excess their feelings of grief. A woman of this type, who had just lost her father, rolled upon the ground, tore her hair, uttered imprecations against all nature, and in her despair would have wished the human race annihilated. Were not her vociferations and her cries indicative of delirium in the highest degree?

Reason can sometimes strive more or less successfully against misfortune and succumb only to profound and repeated experiences of bitter sorrow. Pinel refers (see page 56) to the young woman of weak character but cultivated mind who was struck by consternation by the sudden and unexpected loss of her family's fortune and the death of her father.

Her mother, abandoned to despair, lost appetite and sleep and became deranged. To defray the expenses incurred under these circumstances, the young girl sacrificed capital producing an income of eight hundred francs, found herself reduced to living by the work of her hands, and saw the hope of an approaching marriage vanish. These accumulated disasters claimed all her intellectual functions and led to a sort of melancholy stupor of which she could be cured only by the most assiduous care and eight months of treatment in the Salpêtrière hospital.

A perpetual contrast between vice and virtue is displayed by the human family within its domestic life. Pinel points to the contrast between families who prosper over periods of years in order and harmony and those who offer

> . . . a repulsive picture of debauchery, dissension, and shameful distress! This, according to my daily notes, is the most fertile source of the mental alienation which one has to treat in the hospitals.* Here there is an active woman who sees the fruits of her labor and thrift dissipated by a husband given to every sort of excess; there another woman, negligent or degraded, who brings about the ruin of a hard-working man; in still another case, husband and wife are equally blameworthy and plunge into ruin together, and the mental alienation of one of them follows closely upon their loss of all resources. I refrain from disclosing examples of this sort; some do honor to the human race but a great many others present the most disgusting picture and seem to be a disgrace to it.

Sometimes events of extreme cruelty lead to despair and mental alienation. Among his examples Pinel cites the impressive story (see page 56) of the farmer's daughter who, during the Vendée uprising. saw her brothers and parents massacred and, struck with terror and mentally confused, succeeded in escaping from the carnage only to find herself abandoned and deprived of all support.

> Certain principles which have been adopted or contradictory ideas which take strong hold upon the imagination may produce inner conflicts and intense emotions which eventually bring about mental alienation. A young woman reared in accordance with the precepts of a strict morality recognized in her twentieth year the imprudence of having taken a vow of chastity at the age of fourteen, and consented to marriage with all the religious formalities most likely to reassure her fearful conscience. But pious reading and melancholy meditations every day led to scruples and remorse and caused her to seek solitude; she was sometimes found in tears, repeating amid sighs and sobs that she was a miserable woman and that she never should have married. She was nevertheless a tender wife and became the

---

* It is especially before or during the menstrual period or following childbirth that emotions of every kind are dangerous; this concurrence causes mental alienation to be much more frequent among women than among men. (Pinel's footnote.)

"Q" mother of four children. Difficulties encountered in the nursing of the last one aggravated her condition; her scruples and her melancholy seemed to increase from day to day. Palpitations and syncopes followed, and finally a furious delirium broke out.

The fatigues of war, the hardest and most painful life, heat, cold, hunger, sleep snatched in haste and often followed by several nights without sleep, are very likely to impart masculine vigor to the body; Caesar himself used them to correct or fortify a weak and impaired constitution. But their abrupt termination and the transition to apathetic inactivity are as demoralizing as they are physically debilitating; they cause all the vital functions to languish, produce involuntary sadness, a sort of cowardliness, and recurring fears against which one is defenseless. The gradual result is a hypochondria which may become manifest mania.

A very distinguished soldier, after fifty years of active service in the cavalry, had changed during his later years to an opposite way of life and enjoyed all the pleasures of an easy and comfortable life in a pleasant countryside. The respiratory and digestive organs rebelled against this inactivity, being, moreover, weakened by the advance of age, and the result was a periodic and excessive mucous secretion. He became subject to various nervous affections, such as spasms of the extremities, starts while asleep, nightmares, and sometimes flashes of heat in the feet and hands. The disorder soon extended even to his state of mind; he began by experiencing intense emotions for the slightest causes. If, for example, he heard some disease mentioned, he at once thought that he was suffering from it. If, in the intimate society of his friends, mental alienation was spoken of, he believed himself insane and retired to his room, full of dark reveries and apprehensions; everything became for him a cause for fear and alarm. If he entered a house he was afraid the floor would give way and plunge him to destruction. He would not cross a bridge without fear, unless there was a question of fighting and the call of honor was heard. Was this not a state of hypochondria likely to become a state of mania? (3, pp. 32-33).

A young man cannot win the hand of a girl with whom he is desperately in love, and sees his offers disdainfully rejected by the parents. He becomes taciturn, indifferent to all pleasures, subsisting only on suspicions and gloomy forebodings. He flies into a rage on the slightest provocation and sinks alternately

"Q" into discouragement and extreme perplexity. The company of his friends is more and more a burden to him, and the end is a true melancholy delirium.

Sometimes intense agitation recurring constantly and a sort of internal conflict between the inclinations of the heart and religious scruples can bring about melancholy or maniacal delirium. A young girl, sixteen years old, reared according to the strictest principles, is placed in a laborer's home to learn embroidery; there she receives the attentions of a young man of the same age and finds herself exposed to all his advances; pious sentiments resulting from her education reawaken strongly and engage in a sort of internal struggle with her affections. Melancholy ensues with all its fears and perplexities; there is loss of appetite, loss of sleep, and a furious delirium. Taken to the asylum, a victim alternately of convulsive movements and complete mental derangement, she seems to be assailed by the most incoherent ideas, often utters inarticulate sounds or disconnected sentences, speaks of *God and of temptation*. During the first month, she is induced only with the greatest effort to take any food (3, pp. 38-39).

VIII | Pinel as a Psychologist– His Sources

In the eighteenth century, psychology was still taught as the doctrine of the soul; this was considered to be a part of *pneumatology* or doctrine of the spirits, in its turn a part of metaphysics. The *Encyclopédie ou Dictionnaire Raisonné des Sciences, des Arts et des Métiers* by Diderot and d'Alembert can be considered as an authentic source for the examination of the state of human knowledge in the second half of the eighteenth century. The author who prepared the article on psychology—most probably Diderot himself—defined psychology as that part of *philosophy* which deals with the human soul. It was divided into empirical, or experimental, and rational psychology. The former rests on experience, by which it explains the processes which take place in the soul. Rational psychology tries to reach a definition of the soul from which it derives the various faculties and activities of the soul. Psychology was also taught to supplement other parts of philosophy, i.e., natural law, natural theology, practical philosophy, and logic. The study of psychology, says the author, promises the most vivid pleasures to a mind which loves solid and useful knowledge. The greatest happiness man can attain in his life lies in the knowledge of truth insofar as it is associated with the exercise of virtue. Since the soul has to acquire this knowledge and to practice this virtue, a preliminary knowledge of the soul is indispensable. Such were the spirit and the letter of that generation which prepared the French Revolution and which also shaped the minds of the fathers of this country and its constitution. We may also assume that such were the spirit and the letter of the psychology which reached Pinel .

Psychology is listed in the first American edition of the *Encyclopaedia Britannica* (1798) under the entry of "Metaphysics":

... it consists in the knowledge of the intellectual soul in particular; concerning which, the most profound, the most subtile and the most abstract researches, have been made that human reason is capable of; and concerning the substance of which, in spite of all these efforts, it is yet extremely difficult to support any positive opinion with conclusive or probable arguments.

In the course of the nineteenth century psychology severed its original ties with metaphysics to become a branch of the natural sciences, whose methods it adopted integrally. The result was the liquidation of the soul, that age-old unitary concept; it disappeared from the scientific vocabulary around the middle of the nineteenth century under the rising power of materialism and in connection with the political unrest and upheaval which shook the European continent at that time. Subsequently, psychology, once a single though relatively narrow branch of human knowledge, split into several more or less separated areas, of which the last edition of the *Encyclopaedia Britannica* lists no less than eleven: physiological, comparative, genetic, social, abnormal, differential (providing the basis for the selective techniques of vocational and personal psychology), educational, clinical, vocational, industrial, and professional. To these fields one might even add three more, i.e., legal, military, and above all, experimental psychology.

Is there any common denominator to these special fields? It is, I submit, to be found in certain basic tenets which are the criteria of nineteenth-century science, particularly the natural sciences. The latter rest on the power of factual evidences, and these are understood to be observable and demonstrable objectively if not experimentally. The most eloquent witness of this approach is the test, in which the reactions and responses of the tested individual are listed, even calculated, but in which the interpretations and conclusions remain the most difficult and vulnerable areas. The structure of the test reflects the very method psychology borrowed from the natural sciences, particularly from physiology: the concept of man and animals as compounds functioning according to the well-known diagrammatic scheme of incoming stimulus and outgoing reaction. In this respect, psychology remained faithful to the sensualistic tradition.

None of the branches of psychology mentioned above could have been known to Pinel. Though he claimed the human passions to be the sources of mental alienation, Pinel was not a psychologist in the modern sense. He had no more, but also no less, to invest in his "psychological" effort than his great *observational* power and the *reasoning* which rests on this power. But again, if we turn to the *Encyclopédie ou Dictionnaire Raisonné des Sciences, des Arts et des Métiers* for authentic information about the meaning and scope of the terms "observation" and "observer" as conceived and used by the generation of Pinel—and most probably by himself—we must admire the breadth of view and the wealth of experience embodied in the articles on *the observer* and *observation* as they appear in the monumental work of Diderot and D'Alembert.

Diderot and d'Alembert, the editors of the *Encyclopédie ou Dictionnaire Raisonné des Sciences, des Arts et des Métiers*, confessed in their *"Discours préliminaire"* that they looked upon Bacon as their guide and model when they established their own classification of human knowledge. The latter was indeed no more than a slight modification of Bacon's division of learning. Above all, the principle of classification was the same in both, namely, the basic functions of the human mind (i.e., memory, reason, and imagination) determining in their turn the branches of history, philosophy, and poetry. "The sciences," the French authors said, "are branches which grow from the same stem, i.e., human understanding" (21b, p. XXXI). The eminent French Encyclopedists strongly emphasized *the sameness of the principle destined to mark the origin of human knowledge and the links by which they are united.* In other words, their classification was a *cyclopedic order as well as a genealogic tree,* neither of them ever entirely free from arbitrary choice or discretion.

But we may be still closer to the authentic sources from which Pinel drew his concept of observation by turning to the original texts of Condillac, that philosophical and educational figure who shaped the minds of French intellectuals and French society in the eighteenth century. Pinel was an avowed pupil of Condillac's teaching, whose influence Pinel gratefully acknowledged more than once. Here are the English versions of *Condillac's crucial texts on observation*:

> Our first objective, the one we must never lose sight of, is the study of the human mind, not to discover its nature, but to know its workings, to observe with what artistry they are *devised,* and how we should direct them in order to acquire all the intelligence of which we are capable. It is necessary to go back to the origin of our ideas to trace their genesis—follow them to the limits which nature has set for them—to determine thereby the extent and boundaries of our knowledge and renew all human understanding (16, Introduction to the *Essai sur l'origine des connaissances humaines*).

"Q" It is only by means of observations that we can make these investigations successfully, and we should aspire only to discover a primary experience which no one can call in question and which is sufficient to explain all the rest. It must show palpably what is the source of our knowledge, what are its materials, by what principle they are put to work, what instruments are employed therein, and in what manner they should be used (16, vol. I, p. 4). I have, it seems to me, found the solution of all these problems in the association of ideas, whether with signs or among themselves; and it can be judged as the reading of this work proceeds.

It is apparent that my intention is to refer to a single principle all that concerns human understanding, and that this principle will be neither a vague proposition, nor an abstract maxim, nor a gratuitous supposition: but a continuous experience, all the consequences of which will be confirmed by new experiences.

It would be preposterous to deny to a medical philosopher of the caliber of Pinel—the first interpreter of mental alienation by the action of human passions and its cure by psychological means—it would be preposterous to deny him a place in psychology. But which area? Since he claimed no other exploratory power than *observation*, it is the latter alone which *emerges as instrumental in his psychological design and endeavor*. In brief, he should have expanded his observations to their maximum, hoping to delimit an area of uncontested observational power applied to mental alienation and its roots. His observational power might thus have reached those inner experiences and manifestations which do not lie open to the senses, but which cannot be discarded from the whole of mental dynamics. He could have learned from Galen, who recalled and brought into relief the teaching of the dogmatists, who, contrary to the empiricists, held that therapeutical indication, i.e., the choice of the right remedy, cannot dispense with those things which are inaccessible to the senses. But Pinel, though occasionally doing justice to some psychosomatic views and psychotherapeutical successes achieved by Galen (56), was rather reluctant to learn from the latter and was openly hostile to those currents in medical history known as Galenism. We are on firmer ground when turning to Pinel's own seventeenth century countrymen and moral philosophers, above all, to La Rochefoucauld. On a previous occasion (47) I called the latter the *"seventeenth century pioneer of unmasking psychology."* On another occasion (48) a genealogy of authors was cited by me extending from

Montaigne to La Rochefoucauld, J. J. Rousseau, Nietzsche and, of course, S. Freud, all of whom tried *to uncover and decipher man's hidden thought*, which is frequently, though not successfully, denied by man's own words and overt behavior. Montaigne left but one book, rightly claimed by him the first book, the sole subject of which was the author himself. There is embodied in his *Essays* the whole spirit of the Renaissance, its sense of realism as well as its daring striving for the conquest of new worlds, material and intellectual ones.

According to a recent interpreter of Montaigne (12), "His influence, on the whole, has worked toward 'free thought' and 'naturalism.'" I quote but one passage from Montaigne's *Essays*:

Compassion is a spur to clemency, and prudence to preserve and govern ourselves is aroused by fear; and how many brave actions have been born of ambition? How many by presumption? In a word, there is no eminent and sprightly virtue without some irregular agitation. Should not this be one of the reasons that moved the Epicureans to discharge God from all care and solicitude of our affairs, because even the effects of His goodness could not be exercised in our behalf, without disturbing His repose, by the means of passions, which are so many spurs and instruments pricking on the soul to virtuous actions? (32, Vol. 2, Chap. 12).

As to La Rochefoucauld,* I quote no more than *the motto with which he prefixed his Moral Maxims: "Our virtues are our vices in disguise."*

* The terms which La Rochefoucauld uses to lead up to his unmasking tendencies are "dissimulate" and "disguise." The following passage expresses in a way that could hardly be improved the humanitarian implications of these unmasking tendencies: "One may talk to them about the things that concern them, but only to the extent that they permit it, and in this one must keep strictly within bounds; there is courtesy and sometimes even humaneness in not penetrating too deeply into the innermost recesses of their hearts; they often have difficulty in revealing all that they know, and they have still more when one discerns what they do not know . . . we wish to be informed up to a certain point, but not in every respect, and there are all sorts of truths that we are afraid of knowing . . . . One is right, as a rule, in not wishing to be examined too closely, and there is hardly a man who would wish to let himself be seen as he is in every respect . . . No one views with the same eye that which concerns him and that which does not; our taste, then, is guided by the inclination of *amour-propre and* temperament, which provide us with new opinions and subjects us to an infinite number of changes and uncertainties. . . ." NOTE: All these quotations are taken from Chapter X *"Des Goûts des Réflexions diverses."*

I cannot resist the temptation to quote a somewhat lengthy passage from Rousseau's *Discourse on the Origin of Inequality*:

"Q" We may admire human society as much as we please; it will be none the less true that it necessarily leads men to hate each other in proportion as their interests clash, and to do one another apparent services, while they are really doing every imaginable mischief. What can be thought of a relation in which the interest of every individual dictates rules directly opposite to those the public reason dictates to the community in general—in which every man finds his profit in the misfortune of his neighbour? There is not perhaps any man in a comfortable position who has not greedy heirs, and perhaps even children, secretly wishing for his death; not a ship at sea of which the loss would not be good news to some merchant or other; not a house which some debtor of bad faith would not be glad to see reduced to ashes with all the papers it contains; not a nation which does not rejoice at the disasters that befall its neighbours. Thus it is that we find our advantage in the misfortunes of our fellow-creatures, and that the loss of one man almost always constitutes the prosperity of another. But it is still more pernicious that public calamities are the objects of the hopes and expectations of innumerable individuals. Some desire sickness, some mortality, some war, and some famine. I have seen men wicked enough to weep for sorrow at the prospect of a plentiful season; and the great and fatal fire of London, which cost many unhappy persons their lives or their fortunes, made the fortunes of perhaps ten thousand others. . . . Let us penetrate, therefore, the superficial appearances of benevolence, and survey what passes in the inmost recesses of the heart. Let us reflect what must be the state of things when men are forced to caress and destroy one another at the same time; when they are born enemies by duty, and knaves by interest. It will perhaps be said that society is so formed that every man gains by serving the rest. That would be all very well, if he did not gain still more by injuring them. There is no legitimate profit so great, that it cannot be greatly exceeded by what may be made illegitimately; we always gain more by hurting our neighbours than by doing them good. Nothing is required but to know how to act with impunity; and to this end the powerful employ all their strength; and the weak all their cunning (58, pp. 222-223) .

In another of Rousseau's major writings, we find the following passage, which reads like an anticipation, though a crude one indeed, of sublimation and the *unmasking* of the purely instinctive genesis of science:

> You may glance at world history, you may give priority to philo-sophical investigations over unreliable reports, but you will never discover an origin of human knowledge which would meet the idea one likes to have about it. Astronomy originated from superstition; rhetoric from ambition, hate, flattery, and lies; geometry from avarice; physics from vain curiosity; all human knowledge and even morals spring from arrogance. Thus science and art owe their origins to our vices; we would be less in doubt about their benefit, were they due to our virtues (60, Vol. 17 p. 253).

It remains true, however, that Pinel did not attack the problem of unmasking psychology *systematically*. But it was the major subject of the letter which he addressed to his brother on the first of January, 1779. The integral text of the letter has been translated into English and reads as follows:

> On the proposed question: "To determine whether progress in legislation has kept pace with that in the sciences and the arts," one may take either the negative or the affirmative side and support it equally well with facts. This is what will always happen when the question is vague and when those who propose it have not taken care to keep in view a specific object.
>
> First of all, if one glances at the legislative systems which have flourished on earth, one will see that, in the establishment of society, each one has preceded enlightenment in the sciences and arts, which presupposes a people civilized and brought by circumstances and the passage of time to that maturity and leisure which bring letters to flower. When Lycurgus gave laws to Sparta and produced in that republic such a wealth of great men through wisely planned institutions, he was not impelled to this by the flourishing state of letters. This law-giver of great and patriotic soul, wishing to make his fellow citizens happy, travelled to Crete and meditated deeply upon man's nature, grasping on his travels every ray of enlightenment. Inflamed with love of his country, he pursued with the greatest ardor the

"Q" project of reforming the customs of the people and establishing the wisest institutions. If he took the trouble to collect the writings of Homer and make them known to his country, it was only to inspire the martial courage necessary to a warlike people. In short, an ardent patriotism illumined by knowledge of human nature was his only guide.

As for Solon, who gave laws to Athens, he was concerned alone with the knowledge of government and politics, and in Greece we see that practical philosophy, ethics, and politics were especially cultivated even before the natural sciences and letters had cast the slightest shadow. It seems that the first reflections of man must fall upon the means of making himself happy and causing the society in which he lives to flourish; it is not necessary to have great knowledge of the human heart to realize that those customs which form great characters are the only means of producing a durable and flourishing government. The more man divests himself of personal interests and the more concerned he is with the general good, the more ardently he contributes to attaining it. Moral philosophy, therefore, appears to be the best foundation for an excellent legislation. From this came the large number of schools of philosophers which had their cradle in Greece. You can read, concerning the lives of the ancient philosophers, the Latin translation of Diogenes Laercius and Plutarch on the lives of Lycurgus and Solon.

If you really wish to know the progress of legislation among the Romans, you should read the reflections of Montesquieu on the causes of the greatness and the decline of the Romans; you will see that this ancient senate, whose political skill was so fatal to other nations, was not lighted by the torch of sciences and letters, but based its conduct upon the models transmitted to it by the Greeks, upon its profound reflections and that patriotic enthusiasm with which it was inflamed. When letters were so flourishing, in the reign of Augustus, this was only a refinement of politics, an adroit way of covering with flowers the chains imposed upon its citizens. By multiplying the sources of enjoyment, by offering to the mind and heart a thousand different pleasures, by offering a taste of the charm of letters, this skillful, ambitious man diverted the Romans from patriotic interests and weakened the resilience of their souls. He should not be judged in accordance with the flatteries of Horace, Virgil, and so on; we should see him as he was, compare his reign with those

"Q" which preceded it, and we shall see whether Roman legislation followed the progress of letters.

China, an empire no less ancient, is perhaps a model of legislation. Nowhere has what one calls concern for the common good been so general, but this is related to the tradition that the empire is a large family of which the emperor is the father: everyone contributes to the public welfare and there is an admirable police force to prevent crime and encourage virtue. Nevertheless, science and letters, though cultivated from the most remote antiquity, are still in a state of mediocrity.

One would seek in vain for models of legislation in the hot climates of India, Persia, Turkey, Arabia, and the regions of Africa. We know that in all times languor and mental inactivity have been their lot, that despotism trifles with the lives and the possessions of the subjects. Servile fear is the soul of these governments, and it is only the caprice of the despot which causes laws to come into being and to disappear.

If Arabia constituted an exception to the rule, if the powerful genius of Mahommed and of some of the caliphs established laws in conformity with the nature of the climate and the inhabitants, if the disciples of Mahommed became so formidable and threatened to invade the whole known earth, it was only to the great genius of certain caliphs that were due these elevated views and the manly conduct which caused so many powers to tremble. The sciences and arts flourished only at later times, when the empire was on the point of crumbling. Caliph Harun-al-Rashid, approximately a contemporary of Charlemagne, caused them to flourish in Babylon; but can we attribute to their progress the rise and aggrandizement of the empire of the caliphs, since it had already reached its highest point?

If we pass on then to Europe and examine the legislation from the most remote antiquity, we shall see that after the Romans the greatest peoples to appear in this part of the earth were the Germans. One cannot, however, say that letters were cultivated among this people, whose profession was entirely military and who were led by the Druids, a sect of fanatic priests, who naturally took advantage of the influence given them by religion; nevertheless, the spirit of pride and independence dominant in this people gave rise to laws very favorable to liberty. One can

"Q" study their institutions in the admirable work of Tacitus, *De Moribus Germanorum*.

It is perhaps from the Germans that the English derived their legislative code, which is the only one in Europe worthy of attention, and the one in which the right of the individual is best combined with that of the prince. Now, one would not say that the English owe their legislation to the flourishing state of the sciences and arts, which it preceded by several centuries. When the proud inhabitants of this island distinguished themselves by their genius and their talents, their legislation was all that it could be. It was patriotism which sustained them in their reverses and which enabled them to discover resources; it is to the ardor with which they administer public affairs that they owe their modern institutions, their commerce, their agriculture; and if knowledge of the natural sciences gave rise to learned institutions and contributed to perfecting them, it must be admitted that the very foundation of their legislation is due to quite different causes. You can get an idea of the laws of England from Montesquieu's *L'esprit des Lois*.

There has been much instability in French laws (although one can see that Charlemagne in his famous capitulary attempted to bring order into them), for the military spirit of our nation produced laws most contrary to humanity. The princes, in general, in order to gain the favor of the nobles, gave them as a military reward the right to oppress the people with impunity.

Charlemagne's successors, unworthy of this great man and without capacity for ruling, opened the way for independence and feudal anarchy; the lords became subordinate tyrants in their estates, as the counts and dukes had become masters in the governments which the princes had entrusted to them. For years France, Germany, Poland, etc., were merely theaters of brigandage and rapine, because of the continual wars the subordinate tyrants waged among themselves. Finally, the crusades, in spite of their folly, nevertheless had, in a certain respect, good effects: the lords transferred most of their lands, and their vassals were freed from the yoke; the princes acquired greater power, etc., (see a book entitled *Tableau de l'Histoire Moderne* in these volumes). Our legislation, and that of many other nations, is still in chaos. What matters the flourishing state of the sciences, the philosophical tone of the century? The interests of those

"Q" who govern are still remote from the noble and elevated views of the truly enlightened man; I see it here in Paris. The philosophers live in oblivion and retreat, or if they appear from time to time in society, it is only because people enjoy their conversation. Besides, their principles are opposed to those of society; the latter regards them merely as bizarre creatures. They are especially isolated from the government and from the chambers of the princes, who like only those who are likely to flatter them and to extend their power. It must be admitted, nevertheless, that the host of philosophical writings which appear shed light upon certain subjects, and from time to time bring about some useful revolution. But what is this, if one compares it with the whole system of legislation?

The immortal work of Montesquieu is undoubtedly well-suited to providing instruction on legislation, and recently the Empress of Russia reformed her code in accordance with this excellent model; but this precious literary monument will rarely be consulted. It is chance, circumstances, a fortuitous course of events, or the passions and customs of persons in authority which determine the form of government and institutions.

I have not spoken of the famous republics of Switzerland, Holland, Venice, or the United States of America; but if in the latter we must except Pennsylvania, where the illustrious Penn, who had an enlightened mind and a patriotic heart, established very wise legislation, we see always the cause which served as a basis for the laws. In general, the English colonies were formed in accordance with the English constitution, and the old republics which still shine in Europe were founded in stormy times and owe their institutions to the sad necessity for maintaining themselves in the face of formidable powers which tried to oppress them and whose efforts increased their love of liberty and their inner resources. To discuss all these subjects would demand profound knowledge and research; but you can find all that you need, in relation to the present question, in the book by Abbé Raynal: *Histoire philosophique et politique de l'établissement des Européens aux deux Indes.*

You can see, by what I have just sketched lightly for you, that it would be necessary to decide the question in the negative, but although it might be possible to assemble declamations and vain arguments in favor of the contrary opinion, nothing sound could be accomplished except by adopting another viewpoint.

"Q" If you work on this subject, you should first make an outline, then sketch a rough draft on paper, thinking carefully about each article in particular and connecting the ideas closely; then, in the fourth place, review the whole and consider the style and the development of the thoughts. There is no other method for doing it well.

After you have thought about the present subject, if anything perplexes you, please write to me.

Affectionately, your brother,

Pinel*

Pinel and Rousseau

In following his humanitarian calling, Pinel did more than simply obey the voice of nature. Again, he proved to be a son of the eighteenth century and seemed to listen to one of its most illustrious, though contested, representatives. It is true that the *name* of Rousseau does not occur in Pinel's writings, with the exception, however, of one passage (3, XI), in which he deplored Rousseau's caustic humor and disdainful attitude toward physicians. But there are other passages from which Pinel emerges almost as a faithful follower of Rousseau and of the thesis so significant of Rousseauism, of *the pathogenic effect of cultural institutions and restrictions*. I can do no better than to cite these passages side by side, the first from Pinel:

"Q" A constitution, weak from the onset, or deteriorated through the excesses of youth, or still worse, through their perpetuation in the decline of life. The tremendous rise of man's ambitions, striving for honor, wealth, academic and literary distinctions, fame; a sedentary life, detrimental to the secretions and muscular strength, while overeating and intemperance produce a hyper-secretion of the nutritive juices; the numerous artificial

* The reason for the translation of this letter may not be immediately apparent to the reader; however, its text reveals something of Pinel as a *teacher*, as a *psychologist* attempting to unmask the true sources of man's legislative activity, even as an *historian*. In this respect, it is closely related to the introductions to two of his major works: that of the *Traité médico-philosophique sur l'aliénation mentale*, in which he traces the history of the treatment of the insane, and that of *La médecine clinique*, in which he traces the history of medical doctrines.

"Q' stimulations of weakening functions, lack of sleep, overworking, excessive study, intense worries, never-ending troubles, the turmoil of passions in families where tranquillity, order and harmony should reign (2a, pp. CXXXIV, CXXXV).

Let us compare, without prejudice, the state of civilized man with that of the savage and let us ask ourselves whether civilization has given a new opening to suffering and death, not to mention the wickedness, needs, and miseries of civilized man. Consider the mental strain which destroys, and the violent passions which depress and exhaust us, the exceedingly heavy toll laid on the shoulders of the poor, the still more dangerous softness in which the rich indulge, some dying of their needs, others of their excesses. Think about the monstrous admixtures of our food, their pernicious spices, the corrupted nutriments, falsified drugs, the mischief of those who sell and the mistakes of those who administer them, the poisoned vessels in which they are prepared. Look at the epidemics produced by the foul air in a closely packed population, at those precipitated by our soft way of life, the alternate passing from the climate of our dwellings to the outdoor atmosphere, our clothing which we put on and off without due precaution, and at all the manifold care we give to ourselves, which leads to necessary habits the neglect of which may destroy life and health. Do not forget the incendiaries and earthquakes, destroying entire cities and thousands of lives. Take together the dangers with which all these causes threaten us permanently and you will realize the heavy toll we have to pay to nature for the contempt of her lessons" (60, Note 9, Vol. 3 p. 313).

Of still greater significance for the problem of the natural or emotional sources of Pinel's endeavor must be those passages in Rousseau's writings which reveal the sentimental constituents of the author's views on human nature, the foundations of his social life, morality, and education. I cite from the *Dissertation on the Origin and Foundations of the Inequality of Mankind*:

It is then certain that compassion is a natural feeling which, by moderating the violence of love of self in each individual, contributes to the preservation of the whole species. It is this compassion that hurries us without reflection to the relief of those who are in distress; it is this which in a state of nature supplies the place of laws, morals, and virtues, with the advantage that none are tempted to disobey its gentle voice; it is this which will always prevent a sturdy savage from robbing a weak child or a feeble old man of the sustenance they may have acquired with pain and difficulty, if he sees a possibility of providing for himself by other means; it is this which, instead of inculcating that sublime maxim of rational justice, *Do to others as you would have them do unto you,* inspires all men with that other maxim of natural goodness, much less perfect indeed, but perhaps more useful, *Do good to yourself with as little evil as possible to others.* In a word, it is rather in this natural feeling than in any subtle arguments that we must look for the cause of that repugnance which every man would experience in doing evil, even independently of the maxims of education. Although it might belong to Socrates and other minds of the like craft to acquire virtue by reason, the human race would long since have ceased to be, had its preservation depended only on the reasonings of the individuals composing it (59, p. 345).

As early as 1951, in my first paper on Pinel, I considered it a dubious if not hopeless undertaking to trace the sources of Pinel's endeavor solely to his humanitarian calling or, in more eloquent and technical terms, to derive the rationale of his endeavor from an irrational, that is to say, a sentimental or emotional matrix. Pinel's achievement—this cannot be affirmed often enough—is an imposing body of diagnostic, prognostic, therapeutic, organizational, reformatory, and educational measures, which he could never have taken by means of natural compassion (*bonté originelle*) alone. In fact, he confessed more than once that to reach his view on mental alienation he had to know, to understand, and to accept the doctrines of Locke and Condillac, and particularly their views on the genesis and faculties of human understanding. It was the latter which provided Pinel with the intellectual weapons to identify, to classify, and to treat mental alienation. But to do this, he had to relinquish gradually the purely natural state of human compassion in order to become an enlightened citizen, equipped with the intelligence, the learning, the prerogatives, and the duties implied in his new condition. Did he know that he did no more than retrace the road by which, in the eyes of Rousseau, man must have passed from the state of nature (*l'état naturel*) to the state of society (*l'état civil*)? Historically speaking, a vast distance separates the two states, but individual man may recover, in a fragment of time, gifts and abilities which take the species an incredible length of time to acquire. In brief, the metamorphosis which Pinel's own original and purely natural feelings had to undergo to merge into an organized and coherent plan of recognizing, distinguishing, and treating mental alienation, was the work of enlightenment and intelligence, that is, of *understanding*. But it is different with Rousseau's savage man who had no such career to open. In fact, in this case the metamorphosis reflects *a natural history of moral* thought. Three stages are distinguished by Rousseau in this history: that of consciousness, that of the growing knowledge of man's relations to his fellow-creatures and of those relations which he discovers as existing between objects, and, finally, the third stage, in which justice, order, virtue, and vice make their appearances in the mind and behavior of the savage man, who in the original state of nature possesses no more than that natural feeling which hurries us without reflection to the relief of those who are in distress.*

None of the transformations described here carries with it the absolute necessity of its coming into existence. "It appears," said Rousseau, "that Providence most wisely determined that the faculties which the savage man potentially possessed should develop themselves only as occasion offered to exercise them in order that they might not be superfluous or perplexing to him by appearing before their time, nor slow and useless when the need for them arose."** Repeatedly, Pinel referred to that "occasion" which sponsored his views on mental alienation and on the passions as its ultimate sources. "The storms of the Revolution," he said in one of the opening sections of his treatise (devoted to the "circumstances favorable to the author's researches upon the subject of insanity"), "stirred up corresponding tempests in the passions of men, and overwhelmed not a few in a total ruin of their distinguished birthright as rational beings." He cited the case of a man who, seized by mania under the impact of the events of the Revolution, at the height of the attack repulsed with brusqueness his child whom he loved dearly at all other times.

It is from the point thus reached that we gain a new access to the meaning of the term and the scope of *moral treatment*. Let us remember that in the introduction to his treatise on mental alienation Pinel warned his readers to consider the passions, which he believed to be the sources of mental alienation, as apart from all morality, and to look upon them as simple phenomena of human life (*"par abstrac-*

---

* In his letter to Christophe de Beaumont, archevêque de Paris.

** In the first part of his *Dissertation on the Origin and Foundation of the Inequality of Mankind*.

tion de toute moralité et seulement comme des phénomènes simples de la vie humaine") . This warning leaves no doubt that Pinel approached the human passions in their purely original vital or natural state. If his treatment had consisted of no more than teaching his patients to assume responsibility for the often violent and destructive manifestations of their passions, he would have taught them to pass from an original, natural state to that of a citizen; in other words, to retrace the natural history of moral thought, with nature standing at the beginning, and morality at the end, of this history. Thus, the alienated individual covers the same road as the alienist; the former elevating his passions, the latter his educational viewpoint from the state of nature to that of society. This state of affairs and the interrelation of physician and patient which it implies, can be expressed neither in terms of a dialogue nor in that of a monologue. Were we allowed to express it in terms of the spirit of music, we would conclude that, to obtain a successful moral treatment, the insane and the alienist would have to act in unison.

A rapid reader may be tempted to identify the natural or original state of the passions (and specifically, compassion) as it is claimed by Rousseau to exist in the savage with the state of the passions that is claimed to exist in the insane person who has not as yet undergone moral treatment. This rapid identification might even extend to the alienist who has not yet placed at the service of his intelligence and enlightenment an organized and coherent plan of moral treatment, and who has neither discovered for himself nor retraced for the benefit of his patients the natural history of moral thought, passing from a simple manifestation of human life through consciousness and reflection, ultimately to end in virtue or vice. The history of modern psychiatry lists more than one author who did not succeed in escaping these rapid and dangerous identifications. It was not always the most enlightened and the best-trained human figure who gave the signal for a return to an allegedly more healthy and more powerful natural or primeval state, and this return all too often unmasked itself as a retreat behind the moral fences of civilization rather than a return to the still-fertile soil of dawning civilization. Though Rousseau is rarely recognized as the source of these identifications, it is only fair to clear his name and his thought from the dangerous transgressions implied in the identifications uncovered above. As far as I know, this restoration has never been made before. In the beginning of the first part of his *Dissertation on the Origin and Foundation of the Inequality of Mankind,* he warns the reader not to confound the savage man with the men we have daily before our eyes. Rousseau stressed, at the earliest possible hour of his doctrine, the limits and limitations of this doctrine. Thus was avoided, at least in his name, the undue veneration of a hypothetical ancestral state or the vainly attempted falling back to a condition which was lost irrevocably with man's first "commodities" and "preferences," above all, with the advent of symbolic thought and articulate language. These commodities (for example, clothes or a dwelling) were not at all necessary for his survival, for which he was equipped with the same wisdom with which nature protected and preserved her other creatures in their natural states. Increasing inequality was the price early man had to pay for the acquisition of the new order of things, physical, psychical and social. But the social virtues and the other faculties which natural man potentially possessed could never develop of themselves, but must require the fortuitous concurrence of many external causes that might never arise, and without which the savage man would have remained forever in his primitive condition. With the latter statement Rousseau had reached a theory of epigenetic evolution in which we distinguish a factor of inner preparedness or prospective tendency (Rousseau's "perfectibility") from a cooperation of outer circumstances (51).

We cannot expect a theory of *evolution* to be a subject of Pinel's endeavor to analyze and to treat mental alienation. The evolutionary view had to wait almost another century before it made its appearance in psychiatry under the then growing influence of psychoanalysis, extending from Freud's own analogy between the neurotic and primitive man to Jung and Storch's discovery of the similarity of schizophrenic thought and that of the savage man, with the appearance and reappearance of *archaic* thinking in both conditions. The evolutionary interpretation of normal and abnormal mental phenomena originated and grew in psychopathology rather than in clinical psychiatry. Pinel's psychopathology was still at an embryonic stage—the observational and descriptive (in brief, the Hippocratic) stage of inquiry directed ultimately towards care and cure, i.e., to actions which could not always be postponed until a deeper understanding and comparative insight into the genesis and symbolic meaning of the symptoms could be reached.

It still remains strange and open to clarification why Pinel never turned to evolutionary interpretations, though it was the eighteenth century that saw the birth of the great theories of evolution and development, i.e., preformation and epigenesis. But we are not prevented from discussing Pinel's thesis in terms of evolution. As I said on a previous occasion (49) an organism is born with its full equipment and with its future functions anticipated in its functional plan. But whenever a behavior takes shape which did not exist before as such, the organism makes a new step in its life history. We are free to emphasize the *potentiality* of future behavior and thus adopt the view of a life already finished from its very beginning. Or we may stress the *actuality* of what did not exist before and thus pave the way to an ever newly formed life. Pinel did not leave unanswered the problem of the potential human faculties waiting for the occurrence of favorable circumstances to become manifest. On one occasion, (Mémoire sur la manie périodique ou intermittente. *Mém. de la Soc. méd. d'émul. de Paris, t.l.,* 1802, p. 47), he spoke in terms of the profound sensibility which, generally speaking, constitutes the character of the maniac susceptible of the most violent emotions and the most intense grief. But still more remarkable was his use of terms such as "constitution," "inner disposition," and "moral disposition," that anticipated terms and concepts which made their appearances in medicine almost a century after Pinel. It is true, however, that the term "disposition" is listed in the fourth edition of the *Dictionnaire de l'Académie Française* (1762) along with a medical connotation; the same holds true for the term "constitution." Of circumstances favorable to the outbreak of a "potential" mania, I have already mentioned the storms of the Revolution. Other precipitating causes were listed by Pinel as unhappy love, domestic difficulties, and social crises of the most various kinds.

Darwinism, in its attempt to explain the origin of new species, refers to variations which are supposed to have arisen incidentally, succeeding each other in a hypothetical march of time, but Darwinism admits only those which may be favorable for the species; in other words, which may fit into the functional plan of the same species. (It is obvious that if they did not fulfill this condition, they would never be integrated into the organism and would be as if nonexistent.) Thus, Darwinism refers to purely mechanical and blind factors as the initial and determining factors of evolution, but finally cannot but have recourse to a coordinated and integrated whole. The approach here attempted, anticipated by Rousseau and prefigured by Pinel, uses the same two constituent elements as does Darwinism, namely, external (incidental) conditions and the functional plan of the organism; but by starting from the very onset with the latter (rather than the former) it avoids a change of method in the same reasoning.

The Origin of the Sciences, After Rousseau

To trace powerful influences of Rousseauism in Pinel's thought, we have to go back to his first major work, the essay which won him the prize of the Academy of Dijon and immediate literary fame. The essay was titled: "Has the Progress of the Arts and Sciences Contributed More to the Corruption or Purification of Morals?" (*Si le rétablissement des sciences et des arts a contribué à épurer les moeurs?*). The English version of the crucial passage reads as follows:

It was an ancient tradition, passed on from Egypt to Greece, that a god who was the enemy of man's repose invented the sciences. What an opinion must the very Egyptians among whom those sciences originated have had of them! Indeed, whether you glance at world history or whether you replace unreliable reports with philosophical investigations, you will never discover an origin for human knowledge corresponding to the idea one would like to have of it. Astronomy was born of superstition; rhetoric of ambition, hatred, flattery, lies; geometry of avarice; physics of vain curiosity; all of them, and even morals, of human arrogance. Thus the sciences and the arts owe their existence to our vices; we should be less in doubt of their benefits, were they due to our virtues. The defect of their origin is only too much reflected in their goals. What should we do with the arts without the luxury which sustains them? Without man's injustice, what would be the need for jurisprudence? What would become of history if there were no tyrants, no wars, no conspirators? Who, in short, would choose to spend his life in sterile contemplation if each one, considering only man's duties and the needs of nature, had no time except for his country, the unfortunate, and his friends? Are we then created to die clinging to the edges of the well into which truth has fallen? This reflection alone should repulse at the first step any man who would seriously seek instruction through the study of philosophy.

How many dangers, how many false approaches there are in scientific investigations! Through how many errors, a thousand times more dangerous than truth is useful, must we pass in order to reach truth! The disadvantage is obvious: for the false is susceptible to an infinite number of combinations, but the truth

"Q" has but one way of being. Besides, who is sincerely searching for it? Even with the best will, by what signs is one sure of recognizing it? In this multitude of opinions, what would be the criterion by which we would judge it?* And, what is most difficult, if by good fortune we ultimately found it, which of us would know how to make good use of it?

If our sciences are vain in the goals which they set for themselves, they are even more dangerous in the effects which they produce. Born of idleness, they in turn foster it; and irreparable loss of time is the first injury which they necessarily inflict upon society. In the political as in the moral sphere, not to do good is to do great wrong; and any useless citizen may be considered a harmful one. Tell me then, you illustrious philosophers, you from whom we learn in what ratio bodies attract one another in the void; what relation the revolutions of the planets bear to the spaces traversed in the same time; what curves have conjugate points, points of inflection, points of reflection; how man sees everything in God; how mind and body correspond without communicating, as two clocks might; what stars may be inhabitated; what insects reproduce in an unusual manner: tell me, I say, you from whom we have received so much sublime knowledge; even if we had never learned any of these things from you, should we be less numerous, less well-governed, less formidable, less prosperous, or more wicked? Reconsider, then, the importance of your accomplishments: and if the efforts of our most enlightened scientists and our best citizens provide us with so little that is useful, tell us what we should think of that host of obscure writers and idle scholars who devour unproductively the state's substance (60, Part I, Vol. 7, pp. 253-4).

The Role of the Association of Ideas According to Pinel

In comparison with the considerable place assigned by Locke to the *association of ideas* in the genesis of madness, the role attributed

* The less one knows, the more one thinks he knows — were the peripatetics in doubt about anything? Did not Descartes reconstruct the universe with cubes and vortices? Is there today even in Europe that most insignificant physicist who would not boldly expound the profound mystery of electricity, which will perhaps be forever the despair of the true philosopher? (60).

by Pinel to this mechanism in mental alienation seems modest indeed. However, he found that "all coherence, all association of ideas seems to be destroyed at the height of mania in some insane persons; they pass rapidly from one idea to another which is sometimes very remote, and the remarks that they make often present unexpected and very strange contrasts, or a confused combination corresponding wholly to the disorder of their ideas" (3, p. 84). This observation is an anticipation and a justification of the famous "flight of ideas," a most characteristic sign frequently observed and described by the generations of alienists who followed Pinel. But, above all, Pinel recognized a dynamic and constructive factor in the association of ideas; he declared that, "We also have the power to detach one or more perceptions or ideas from those which were associated with them and find for them another place in a new combination, which will be all the more firmly established if this bringing together is based upon a large number of relations." Pinel acknowledges here the foundation of the various methods of classification in use in natural history and, consequently, in medicine. Once more, we are keenly aware of Pinel's tendency to link medicine with natural history and its methods, which he took for a model;* at the same time we see Pinel as a philosopher who does not construct nosography in a routine fashion, but who explores the logical foundations of this science, claiming for nosography a philosophical character by the same right that he claimed that character for his treatise on mental alienation. It is always Pinel's philosophical thought which takes precedence over the pure and simple acceptance of experimental data and the facts derived from observation. While apparently self-

---

* For his part, Cuvier, a contemporary of Pinel, in his *Rapport historique sur le progrès des sciences naturelles depuis 1789, et sur leur état actuel* expresses himself in a similar manner. "Medicine", he says, "has taken pride in the support given to it by the natural sciences, and the valuable men who practise it have always devoted themselves ardently to the study of these sciences: it must even be recognized that they owe by far the greater part of their growth to these men." The name of Pinel appears more than once in this report, and the eminent naturalist emphasizes the strict principles of classification which form the basis of Pinel's *Nosographie philosophique*. "Its classes are based," he says, "upon the types of lesions, its orders upon their sites; and the considerations which served as a foundation for the latter classification were the forerunners of those which guided Bichat in his *Recherches anatomiques sure les membranes*." Pinel himself admits that he attempted to introduce into the public teaching of medicine the method followed in all fields of natural history: ". . . strict exactitude in descriptions, precision and uniformity in names, a wise discretion in attaining general views without mistaking abstract terms for reality, a simple, regular classification based invariably upon structural relations or organic functions." Profiting by his own experience, he advises his students to apply themselves early to the study of the natural, and even the mathematical, sciences in order to develop exactness and precision in reasoning.

sufficient, these are in truth subject to the faculties of understanding, the seat and origin of human knowledge according to a line of authors beginning in the seventeenth century with Locke, continuing with Condillac and the encyclopedists to terminate in Pinel, who, in the history of ideas, figures not only as their heir, but also as their successor and, above all, as their trustee.

Pinel's *distrust in metaphysics* as a promising way of approaching the nature, manifestations, and treatment of insanity is revealed by the concluding question raised by him at the end of one of his most telling case histories. It is significant that it was the data of observation that brought him face to face with this fundamental issue. Far from claiming to be primarily a philosopher trying to invade medicine, he always remained a physician deeply rooted in the history and trustworthiness of human thought. This hierarchy of methods has to be kept in mind if one wants to reach an adequate understanding of the meaning and the letter of the title of his treatise as a "medico-philosophical" one.

The case history reads as follows:

> A silversmith, who had the extravagance to believe that he had exchanged his head, was at the same time infatuated with the chimera of perpetual motion. He got his tools and set to work with infinite resolution and obstinacy. It may be easily imagined that the discovery in question was not made. There resulted from it, however, several very ingenious pieces of machinery— such as must have been effects of the profoundest combinations. Are those facts consistent with the doctrine of the unity and individuality of the seat and principle of the human mind? If not, what then must become of the thousands of volumes which have been written on metaphysics? (4, p. 26).

The question which Pinel raised at the end of this case history, was suggested to him by his observations that the faculties of reflection and reasoning, though visibly impaired or destroyed in most cases, might retain, either separately or combined, all their energy, or recover themselves speedily if an object calculated to attract and to fix the attention presented itself. Faculties which do not disappear integrally but only partially must indeed deny their unity and indivisibility. Nor can those faculties which recover speedily have a seat or local residence at first destroyed but restored shortly thereafter. The metaphysical heritage which is questioned in the first of these statements is the belief in the existence of a soul, cherished by all thinkers since the days of the Greeks. The anatomical heritage which is questioned in the second of these statements is that of cerebral localization, which in the days of Pinel was not yet formulated in definite terms, though anticipated in terms of phrenology. The concluding question raised by Pinel implies an answer favorable neither to the doctrine of the unity and indivisibility nor to that of the seat of the human mind. Though nineteenth century science indeed relinquished any dealing with metaphysics and thus justified Pinel's purely observational and experiential view, the same century retained and even developed the doctrine of the seat of the human mind, though in the reshaped terms of the doctrine of cerebral localization, which decomposed the once cherished unity of the human mind into an ever-increasing number of components each of which was ascribed to a correspondingly increasing number of cerebral centers. By the "analytical method" which he borrowed from Condillac,* Pinel might have been well-prepared to accept this doctrine, though his educated thought and reasoning power would have prevented him from compressing the (hypothetical) counterparts of human intelligence or any of its departments into the small compartments of man's brain.

In 1808, a year before the publication of the second edition of Pinel's treatise, the metaphysical heritage was still manifest among naturalists in the most eminent Paris society of higher learning. As I recalled on a previous occasion (42).

When Cuvier, in his report given at the meeting of the Institut de France on April 25, 1808, on the anatomical discoveries of F. J. Gall, rejected any attempt to localize the individual self at a well-defined region of the divisible space, he still expressed himself in the language of his time—the language of humanistic thought and tradition in natural science. When he considered the interaction of the divisible matter and the indivisible self

---

* There is indeed a significant passage in Condillac's *Traité des sensations* (chapter IV, second part) which shows that the apologist of sensationalism and of the analytical method was not immune from that fundamental error in method committed by those adherents of cerebral localization who ascribe a local residence, i.e., a spatial character to precisely those functions, such as the psychical ones, which cannot be expressed in terms of space. The child, says Condillac, in order to discover his body, can no longer perceive his sensations as ways of being of his soul, but must learn to perceive them as modifications of his organs. The ego, instead of being concentrated in the soul, must stretch, expand and, so to speak, repeat itself in all parts of the body. The idea of changing local residences of the ego is unmistakable in this passage.

as inconceivable forever *("hiatus infranchissable dans le système de nos idées et pierre éternelle d'achoppement de toutes les philosophies")*, he could rely on being understood and approved by his learned audience. At the meeting of the Paris Society of Anthropology on March 21, 1861, i.e. 53 years later, Gratiolet could still maintain a similar view, using almost identical terms: the unity of the indivisible (immaterial) self reappeared in the vocabulary of this scientist, well-known for his neuro-anatomical discoveries (the optic radiations). But he now defended a lost cause. When, in 1877, only 16 years later, H. Munk called the behavior of a dog deprived of its occipital lobes mind-blindness *(Seelenblindheit)*, he had to apologize for using the term "mind" *(Seele)*. He felt justified in his terminology by defining mind-blindness as a lack of visual representations, i.e., of the memory images of the visual perceptions. This indeed, was the language of the new era, proud of its break with the past and with metaphysics, not realizing, however, that it just substituted one metaphysics for another.

In brief, Pinel proved to be prophetic in both areas of medical thought discussed by him. The doctrine of the unity and indivisibility of the seat and principle of the human mind did not survive. But it testifies to Pinel's genius to have realized at an early hour the problematic nature of the two presuppositions which he found invalidated by the analysis and history of one of his cases, thus foreshadowing a century of clinical and experimental investigations.

Pinel and Descartes

The name of Descartes does not occur in Pinel's major writings.* The fact is all the more surprising in a philosophically trained and gifted French physician of the eighteenth century. No thinker or scholar of that century could conceivably have bypassed the spirit and the letter of the method and the doctrine conceived and formulated by the most independent thinker on French soil in Pinel's day. More-

*It does occur, however, in Pinel's article "Analyse," published in the *Dictionnaire des Sciences Médicales* (1). During the four years of mostly self-directed medical education spent in Montpellier Pinel was always anxious to avoid opinions and conjectures as substitutes for rigorous observations and to let his judgment be formed rather according to the principle of the Cartesian doubt (28.)

over, the analysis, the classification, and the treatment of the human
passions are given an eminent place in Cartesianism; their pathogenic
role in Pinel's view of mental alienation can hardly be overestimated,
and has been stressed by me repeatedly. Did Pinel not know Descartes's treatise *The Passions of the Soul?* Was Pinel not familiar with
Descartes's *correspondence* with the Bohemian princess, Elizabeth,
and the many passages in these letters devoted to the passions and
their remedies, in brief, to their psychotherapeutical significance?

One can hardly deny Descartes the distinction of having been
the first to sketch a *system* of psychotherapy, thus anticipating the
ideas and the accomplishments of the nineteenth century, accomplishments of which his own century otherwise gave no promise. I
believe that it is possible to identify in the Cartesian system of psychotherapy two very different constituents. If one understands by
psychotherapy a body of rules intended to transform the whole
ground of the disease in question, which is to say of the individual
himself and of his position in relation to society and its moral values,
the first constituent which I am able to identify in the Cartesian
psychotherapeutical device hardly merits the name psychotherapy.
It is no more than a *stratagem* which appears in two versions. In his
letter to Princess Elizabeth, written in May or June 1645, he adopts
the stratagem of *diversion*, recommending that she "divert her imagination and sense impressions as much as possible" from her "dis-
comforts," evidently of psychosomatic nature, chief of which was
sadness, considered a passion by authors of the seventeenth century.

Descartes here referred to the self-observation and self-treatment
of an early indisposition which, in spite of the physician's poor prognosis, he succeeded in overcoming, due to his inclination to look at
events from the angle that made them seem most pleasant and to act
in such a way that his main satisfaction depended on himself alone.
The statement definitely implied a *Stoic* element, despite Descartes'
polemic attitude towards Seneca. In terms of modern psychotherapy,
the Cartesian method emerges as an early design of autosuggestion or
autopersuasion. Being a treatment by psychical means, it also emerges
as a pre-design of a *traitement moral*, though its target was not mental alienation but inner unrest, distress, and their physical after-
effects. He reaffirmed his recommendations in another letter,
addressed to this same person, in July, 1647. He then even used terms
such as "strong persuasion" and "firm belief." Like Pinel, the
authentic originator of "moral treatment," Descartes left room for
the healing power of nature. Though he approved of diet and exercise, he still believed that the remedies of the soul rank highest
among all remedies applied.

Common to all these texts is the disbelief in an immediate and direct suppression of the passions and of the various movements accompanying them, and the belief in the delaying and diverting thoughts and movements. Thus took shape a psychotherapeutical design which denied neither the first principles of a philosophy which saw in man primarily a thinking being, nor the point of departure of its author, who felt that he had reached firm ground only when he had retreated to his conscious thinking and doubting self as the only remaining and unshakable ground. The third maxim of his provisional code of morals was "to habituate myself in the belief that, save our thoughts, there is nothing completely in our power *("qu'il n'y a rien qui soit entièrement en notre pouvoir, que nos pensées")* and so to recognize, in respect of the things which are external to us, that when we have done our best, whatever is still lacking to us is, so far as we are concerned, absolutely impossible of achievement" (19, *Discourse on Method,* Part III, p. 135). The twentieth-century reader trained in the science and power of the unconscious, may be reluctant to accept the efficacy of Descartes' method; but he will not remain unimpressed by the inner coherence of the same thought no less palpable in Descartes' theory of knowledge than in its practical consequences and applications.

Descartes declared all passions to be good by nature *("toutes bonnes de leur nature"*: Article 211 of *The Passions of the Soul)* and that one should only avoid their wrong use or excess. Similarly, he understood that "the utility of all the passions wholly consists in their manner of fortifying and prolonging in the soul the thoughts which it is good it should conserve, and which, lacking their support, might readily have been effaced from it. On the other hand, all the harm they can cause consists in their fortifying and conserving these thoughts beyond what is required, or in their fortifying and conserving others on which it is not good to dwell." In other words, Descartes conceived the passions as *instrumental* in human life, thought, and conduct (36).

This brings us face to face with the thesis of the "use of the passions" *(l'usage des passions)*, a thesis whose origins go back to antiquity. Traces of it are found in the moral writings of Plutarch. We have recently discovered other origins in Galen. However, neither Plutarch nor Galen expressed himself on this subject as specifically and precisely as did Descartes. In Article 52 of *The Passions of the Soul* he states:

The objects which move the senses do not excite diverse passions in us corresponding to all the diversities which are in them, but only in accordance with the diverse ways in which they can injure or profit us, i.e., only in so far as they are, to use a general term, of concern to us. The manner of operation of the passions, one and all, consists in this, that they dispose the soul to will the things which nature tells us are of concern to us, and to persist in so willing . . . (19, p. 306).

In spite of his Cartesian heritage Pinel does not emerge from his *Traité médico-philosophique* as an apologist of the doctrine and the therapeutical principle of the "uses of the passions" shared by more than one philosophically minded physician and writer, Cartesian or not, of the seventeenth century (54, pp. 1-74). We must even conclude from some of his interpretations that Pinel occasionally had recourse to the ancient therapeutical method expressed by the maxim *contraria contrariis curantur.* The phrase generally refers to the principle of treating diseases by remedies having properties opposed to those of the disease (7, p. 73). The same author (Caelius Aurelianus), when discussing chronic cases of bleeding states: "The very fact that a case is complicated means that it generally requires contrary remedies to combat the contrary states of disease" (7, p. 655).

The following quotation from Pinel's treatise on insanity bears witness to the tendency of the eminent alienist to adopt, if only at times, for the treatment of passions the once much cherished maxim of *contraria contrariis.* But another passage of Pinel's treatise definitely reveals the therapeutical design embodied in the two letters addressed by Descartes to the Princess Elizabeth. In his letter of May or June, 1645, Descartes confessed that there is only one remedy, and that consists in diverting our imagination and our senses as much as possible and in using only our understanding in considering the enemies who are within us and with whom we must live; the "enemies" evidently being the state of suffering and the symptoms which the princess must have described in her own letter. He drew the picture of a "person who would have an infinity of valid reasons for suffering but who would make every effort to divert the imagination to such an extent that these reasons would never be an object of thought, except when a pressing need would arise, and that all other moments be devoted only to objects capable of bringing contentment and joy. . . ."

One can hardly escape the impression that here again Descartes drew on Stoic sources. It remains true that the Stoic did not simply *divert* the imagination from the suffering for which a person may have "an infinity of valid reasons." It remains equally true that the same person tried to become superior to pleasure and pain and indifferent to fortune. But the terms in which Seneca (64) described the resulting "constant cheerfulness" and "inner joys," the "peace and exaltation of a mind now safely anchored," are the very same terms in which Descartes expressed the *effects* intended by his first therapeutical design, namely, those of "contentment and joy." The difference between the Stoic and the Cartesian design lies in the fact that the former is expressed in the more *global* terms of one's "own resources," and "inner joys," while the Cartesian remedy, using a more *discriminative* thought, consists in "diverting our imagination and our senses as much as possible" and in using only our understanding in considering "the enemies within us" (i.e., the discomfort). The passage from the Stoic to the Cartesian therapeutical design thus reflects the passage from a merely pragmatic to a more refined and theoretical way of thinking; in a sense, it reflects the history of human thought from antiquity to the seventeenth century, and an approximation to a classification of human knowledge, from the experience by the senses to the judgment by the understanding.

More than once Pinel qualified his method as an analytical one. The analytical method adopted by Pinel, in conformity with the teaching of Condillac, implied the mental process of tracing compound diseases to their elements or simple diseases. In no area of his investigations did he prove to be more Cartesian. Though he never acknowledged his Cartesian heritage in explicit terms, he made it easy for his reader to trace the Cartesian sources from which he drew and on which his whole method of investigation rested as on its foundation stones. These sources are to be found in the precepts or rules of the Cartesian method as they are described in the second part of the *Discourse on Method*. The first of these precepts was to accept nothing as true which he did not know to be such; that is to say, scrupulously to avoid precipitance and prejudice, and in the judgments he passed to include nothing additional to what had presented itself to his mind so clearly and so distinctly that he could have no occasion for doubting it. The second of these precepts was to divide each of the difficulties he examined into as many parts as might be required for its adequate solution. The third, to arrange his thoughts in order, beginning with the simplest and easiest things to know, so that he might then ascend little by little, as it were step by step, to the knowledge of the more complex, and, in doing so, to assign an order of thought even to those objects which are not of themselves in any such order of precedence. And the last, in all cases to make enumerations so complete, and reviews so general, that he should be assured of omitting nothing (19). The second precept of the method (i.e., to divide the difficulties to better resolve them) is closely related to the third precept (to start from what is simplest and easiest and to ascend to what is compound). An eminent interpreter (20) of the *Discourse on Method* believes that the second and the third precepts contain in themselves the entire method; in fact, they appear as the two constituents of the same rule in the text of the *Rules for the Guidance of our Mental Powers (Regulae)*. It is these two precepts which emerge as the most significant and crucial ones in any attempt to discover the epistemological structure of Pinel's views on mental alienation, which are thoroughly Cartesian and which are rooted in the three fundamental processes of division, simplification, and enumeration. The twentieth-century reader may be reluctant to accept and to revitalize the distinction between simple and compound diseases. He has learned that simple or isolated functions and dysfunctions are found only when artificially produced in a living organism subject to experimentation. He has also learned that the genesis and the structure of each symptom imply the cooperation of all the parts in a living organism (40, pp. 17-29). Should we then dismiss Pinel's views and method as obsolete? We believe them to be the necessary steps to the final solution and to carry the full weight of a *historical* truth which often, though not always, reveals the weakness but also the strength of a beginning, a promise, and an annunciation.

Pinel Stresses the Need for Diversion

Pinel maintains that "A profound knowledge of man's nature and of the general character of melancholics has always clearly indicated the necessity for administering profound shocks (*ébranlements*) to them to produce a powerful diversion from their gloomy thoughts and to make forceful and long-continued impressions upon all their external senses." Pinel defines the goal that must be set in all public or private institutions for melancholics in the following terms:

> ... patience, firmness, humane feeling in the manner of directing them, continuous watchfulness in the wards to prevent outbursts of anger and exasperations, pleasant occupations varied according to differences in taste, various types of physical exercise, spacious quarters among trees, all the enjoyments and tranquillity of country living, and from time to time soft and

melodious music, all the easier to obtain since there is almost always in these establishments some distinguished musician whose talents languish for want of exercise and cultivation (3, pp. 258-260).

Generally speaking, the twentieth century reader will not find in Pinel's observations any anticipation of the substance and vocabulary of the different schools of psychotherapy of the nineteenth and twentieth centuries. The psychotherapeutic spirit of Pinel is a free and relaxed though watchful one, but it is above all flexible and always adapted to the individual, to his resources, his situation and the stage of the disease. The methods used are those of education and strategy rather than those of a more or less orthodox doctrine. The concept of the sick as it appears in Pinel's work is simply the concept of man, and the concept of man merges with that of humanity, still in accordance with the spirit of the eighteenth century.

Pinel, while granting to the passions a decisive role in the genesis of mental alienation, neither neglected nor failed to recognize the participation of human understanding. If there still remains the slightest doubt on this subject, one has only to do justice to that important constituent element of his doctrine which he calls *method*. What is method? Descartes defined it in the fourth of his *Rules for the Guidance of our Mental Powers*. By method Descartes intended "to signify rules which are certain and easy and such that whosoever will observe them accurately will never assume what is false as true, or uselessly waste his mental efforts, but gradually and steadily advancing in knowledge, will attain a true understanding of all those things which lie within his powers" (19, p. 15). It is obviously understanding which emerges as the source of method and of rules.

Considering his education, his philosophical apprenticeship and structure, and considering the spirit of his century, Pinel must have been acquainted with this passage.

If it is true that Descartes remained his model, sharing with Locke the moulding of the spirit and philosophical glory of the eighteenth century, it is no less true that Pinel is in this respect a disciple of Condillac. In the first chapter of his *Traité médico-philosophique sur l'aliénation mentale*, a chapter entitled "General Plan of the Work," Pinel hopes "to apply the analytical method with greater success to this disease." However, he does not define this method. It was not until seven years later, on publication of his *Nosographie philosophique ou la méthode de l'analyse appliquée à la médecine* (1798), that he was to quote literally (in the introduction to the first and second editions) the definition given by Condillac in his *Logique*:

"To analyze is merely to observe successively the qualities of an object in order to place them in the mind in the same order in which they exist. . . ."

Analysis of thought is no different from that of external objects:

"You break it up in the same way; you retrace the parts in successive order in order to reestablish them in corresponding order; you perform this composition and decomposition in conformity with the relations between things, as principal and subordinate; and, since one would not analyze a landscape if the sight did not embrace the whole of it, neither would one analyze one's thought if the mind did not embrace the whole of it. In both cases, it is necessary to see everything at the same time; otherwise one could not be sure of having seen all the parts one after the other."

Toward the end of the introduction to the *Nosographie*, Pinel believed it necessary to emphasize once more "all the strictness of the term," that is to say, of the analytical method:

. . . one brings together several observed facts of the same sort; one discards all considerations concerning variations of age, constitution, climate, and one thus reaches directly and without deviation the true notion of the species, whether simple or complex. Symptoms common to several species also form, by their combination, a complex and abstract idea, which is that of the genus. The characteristics of orders result from the combination of symptoms which are proper to several genera, and those of classes originate likewise from the affinities existing between different orders.

We see that ultimately the analytic method culminates in *classification*.

Pinel and Galen

After citing, in the introduction to the first edition of his *Traité médico-philosophique*, the views of Hippocrates, Aretaeus, Celsus, and Caelius Aurelianus, Pinel finds it astonishing, as we already know (see page 33), that

"Q". . . principles so enlightened and so fertile in useful applications should not have shown further development during the long centuries following, especially in the regions of Greece and Italy where insanity is so frequent and recurs in such varied forms. But the solution of this problem is easy and is found in a brief reflection upon the general course of the human mind. The talent for observation, left to itself, a stranger to intrigue and the art of gaining prestige, is readily appreciated by people of taste and wins the veneration and esteem of enlightened men of all times and all places; an impact upon the minds of men in general, a striking popularity, is most often the result of the brilliant qualities of new systems, of a rare skill in showmanship. Galen had this advantage over the observers of whom I was just speaking, and this is doubtless one of the greatest obstacles encountered by the branch of medicine dealing with mental alienation.

An intrinsically psycho*therapeutical* constituent is undeniable in the following two observations reported by Galen in his treatise (56), the genuineness of which has never been questioned:

"Q" When I was returning home from Rome, I traveled together with a friend of mine from Gortyna in Crete. This friend was in other respects an estimable person, because he was simple, friendly, good, and anything but miserly. But he was so prone to anger that he used to assail his servants with his hands and even sometimes his feet, but far more frequently with a whip or any piece of wood that happened to be handy.

When we were in Corinth, we decided to send all our baggage and all the servants, except two, from Cenchreae to Athens by ship, while we would hire a cart for our journey overland by way of Megara. Indeed, when we had passed through Eleusis and were coming to the Thriasian Plain, he asked the servants (who were following the cart) about a piece of luggage, but they could give him no answer. He fell into a rage. Since he had nothing else with which to strike the young men, he picked up a good-sized sword in its scabbard and came down on the heads of both of them with the sword, scabbard and all. Nor did he bring down the flat side (for in this way he would have done no great damage) but struck with the cutting edge of the sword. The blade cut right through the scabbard and inflicted two very

"Q" serious wounds on the heads of both—for he struck each of them twice. When he saw the blood pouring forth in abundant streams, he left us and quickly went off to Athens on foot for fear that one of the servants might die while he was still present. We got the wounded men safely to Athens.

But my Cretan friend heaped charges on his own head. He took me by the hand and led me to a house; he handed over his whip, stripped off his clothes and bade me to flog him for what he had done while in the violent grip of his cursed anger—for that is what he called it. When I laughed (and this was a reasonable reaction), he fell on his knees and begged me to do what he asked. It was very clear that the more he kept importuning me and asking to be flogged, the more he was making me laugh. When we had wasted enough time in begging and laughing, I promised him that I would flog him if he would himself grant me the one very small thing which I was going to ask. When he did promise, I urged him to pay attention to me while I had a few words to say to him, since this was my request. When he had promised that he would do so, I spoke to him at some length and admonished him that it was necessary to train the irascible element within us. This is the way, obviously, that I flogged him and not in the way he asked. After I had instructed him, I went away.

That friend of mine, then, took thought for himself and in a year he became a much better man. Even if you should not become much better, be satisfied if in the first year you have advanced and shown some small measure of improvement. If you continue to withstand your passion and to soften your anger, you will show more remarkable improvement during the second year; then, if you still continue to take thought for yourself, you will notice a great increase in the dignity of your life in the third year, and after that, in the fourth year, the fifth, and so on. A man does everything for many years in succession that he may become a good physician, or public speaker, or grammarian, or geometer. Is it a disgrace for you to toil for a long time that you may one day be a good man? (56, pp. 39-41).

The second observation reads as follows:

   . . . I diagnosed the case of a slave who administered the household of another wealthy man, and who sickened in the same way. He was concerned about having to give an account of his expenses, in which he knew that there was a considerable sum wanting; the thought of this kept him awake, and he grew thin with anxiety. I first told his master that there was nothing physically wrong with the old man and advised an investigation to be made as to whether he feared his master was about to ask an account of the sums he had entrusted to him and for this reason was worried, knowing that a considerable amount would be found wanting. The master told me I had made a good suggestion, so in order to make the diagnosis certain, I advised him to do as follows: he was to tell the slave to give him back all the money he had in hand, lest in the event of his sudden death it should be lost, owing to the administration passing into the hands of some other servant whom he did not know, for there would be no use asking for an account from such a one. And when the master said this to him, he felt sure he would not be questioned. So he ceased to worry, and by the third day had regained his natural physical condition . . . (56, pp. 118-119).

These two observations and interpretations are reproduced here to justify Pinel's belief in Galen's "sagacity" and skill in the subject under discussion, though in all probability, Pinel himself was not familiar with the two stories reported by Galen.

In the first of the two cases, the *educational* element of Galen's therapeutical design is obvious; it is implied in the intention "to train the irascible element within us." The instrumentality which thus serves this educational purpose cannot deny its *Stoic* roots. To "withstand your passion and to soften your anger" are terms and suggestions which recall certain texts of Seneca's moral essay "On Anger" (*De ira*).

Seneca lived from about 4 B.C. to 65 A.D., Galen from 130 A.D. to *circa* 200 A.D. Above all, the therapeutical method used by the *Stoics*, and adopted by Galen, was that of a direct and immediate attack of the passions. The uses of rational philosophy in the treatment of discomfort and disease reappeared in the seventeenth century with Descartes' letters to the Princess Elizabeth (36).

I have not been able to trace, in the psychotherapy of insanity as practiced in the early nineteenth century (Reil, Heinroth, and others), any systematic attempts to uncover the roots of the disturbance and the dynamics of its symptoms. Symptoms were attacked immediately. What was intended was the immediate reestablishment of a definite conduct, sanctioned by the rules of society and tradition,

moral standards, and religion. In other words, in the struggle between the mentally ill and reality, the latter was allowed to subdue
the former without delay, without unfolding the abnormal psycho-
dynamics at work, and without a preliminary slow, but progressive,
adjustment that would allow the patient to strengthen his power
and ability to meet the requirements of reality and, above all, to gain
insight into the necessity of complying with them. The direct approach, not too well-timed, necessarily led the psychotherapist to
appeal to logic, reason, and convincing and persuading procedures,
all of which were believed to act directly on the patient and to
produce the intended conduct with no intermediate step (39).

The Galenic approach reaches its maximum by ignoring the
inner experiences of the patient and using his outer behavior as the
sole target of treatment. Thus originates the structure of a *stratagem*
rather than a treatment properly speaking. The method to delay
action in a state of anger is a therapeutical device which I considered
to be a stratagem. It appeared for the first time in Seneca's moral
essay *On Anger* and reappeared in Descartes' correspondence with
the Bohemian princess, Elizabeth. It was the same Descartes who, in
his letter of May or June, 1645, to the princess, designated the manifold sufferings and discomfort with which she was afflicted as "enemies, who are within us and with whom we must live." On the
ground of this Cartesian language I feel strengthened in my own
terminology to call the type of "treatment" under discussion a
stratagem which is a maneuver designated to outwit an enemy in
war. In the second of the two Galenic observations listed above, the
stratagem consisted of the physician's advice to tell the slave to give
back all the money he had in hand, lest, in the event of his sudden
death, it should be lost, owing to the administration passing into
the hands of some other servant. The modern physician would expect
a change in the patient's behavior following the exploration of its
roots or inner sources. The ancient physician hopes for an inner
change in his patient after bringing into play a set of outer acts such
as the circulation of the missing money. I submit that we here grasp
on the narrow level of psychotherapy the fundamental passage from
ancient man to modern man. The two terms here used of ancient and
modern are not intended to convey a merely *chronological* connotation. They stand for the dialectics showing the mutually contradictory *principles* of human action springing either from the force of
outer circumstances or from a man's inner setting and center of
action.

The need for punishment, so obvious in the first of the two cases reported above, marks a strangely modern constituent in the inner structure of Galen's friend; it came to the fore after "the violent grip of his cursed anger" had left him. The "great increase in the dignity of his life" after two years of training, marks the *ethical* component of the whole educational procedure. It reads like an anticipation of a new psychotherapeutical thought (43) and design which we have witnessed in our own day. Galen's repeated insistence upon frequent self-examinations and on guidance by an overseer, supervisor, or tutor is another educational constituent which we identified on a previous occasion in his treatise on the passions and errors of the soul. In neither of the two cases is the working of the unconscious grasped; in this respect the Galenic psychotherapy remains far behind the terminology, the knowledge, and the arsenal of those twentieth century readers and therapists who confess to fail in reaching their patients from the stage of consciousness alone. It is for this reason that we learn nothing about the biographies of Galen's patients. No history is being taken, and in this respect Galen, though a fervent admirer of Hippocrates, violated the fundamental principle of Greek medicine, namely, the history of diseases. He witnessed and assailed the passions and the disease, but he did not explore them. He acted like a general who *attacks* the enemy and uses a stratagem; but our Roman physician did not enter into those long and painful *negotiations* with the disease which we call systematic psychotherapy. The road from antiquity to modern man leads from disease as an *object* of treatment to the changing *subjective* experiences of the patient, who, in a refined sense, emerges as the generator and not simply as the bearer of his disease.

IX | Pinel's Theory of Experience

Pinel on Ideology

It has been stated recently by G. Rosen (57) that the term "ideologues" is commonly applied to a group of French thinkers of the revolutionary and post-revolutionary period who developed and systematized the ideas, outlined by the Abbé Etienne de Condillac during the mid-eighteenth century, into the formal philosophy of ideology. According to Rosen, ideology tended to reinforce and foster the trend to empirical investigation in medicine. Rosen finally concludes that Pinel, who came under the influence of ideology, undertook to reconstruct medical theory by applying to it the analytical method. Pinel said:

> ... ideology could indeed only lose favor in public opinion by comparison with the firm and rigorous course followed by the physical and mathematical sciences; but if it is far from rising to the first rank in the exactness and stability of its principles, should we allow it to fall into oblivion, fail to make it more experimental, and disregard to what extent the study of the functions of human understanding is closely linked to another subject which it is so important to explore deeply, namely, the history and various outcomes of mental alienation? (3, p. 55).

The text of the footnote on pages 299 and 300 of Destutt de Tracy's *Eléments d'Idéologie* (65) leaves no doubt that its author had grasped the fundamental structure of Pinel's view on mental alienation, its genesis and treatment. It is the passions and the atti-

146

tudes *("les opinions des hommes ordinaires")* which emerge not only as roots of mental alienation but also as targets of moral treatment. A passage of still greater significance is to be found in the "Introduction" to Destutt de Tracy's work; it reads as follows:

> . . . the same things cause us to make mistakes in games and in the sciences; well, it is by the same procedures that one learns to speak and that one discovers the laws of the system of the universe, or those of the operations of the human mind, which is to say, all that is most sublime in our knowledge (65, p. 10) .

Pinel's endeavor to trace the history of mental alienation by tracing the workings of the human mind could hardly be expressed in more genuine terms. It is a significant feature of Destutt de Tracy's sensualistic system that he believed all of the basic functions of our organization, i.e., sensibility, memory, judgment, and desire, to be *"sensed,"* thus affirming, though perhaps unwittingly or unwillingly, an intrinsically passive and inert character of human thought. The affirmation is particularly provocative with regard to judgment, which is defined as the necessary consequence of sensibility or the ability to sense relations between our ideas (". . . *c'est la faculté de sentir des rapports entre nos idées; et sentir des rapports c'est sentir)* " (65, p. 48) . Only occasionally, the term *sensed* is abandoned in favor of judgment being *established (jugement "porté")*. But the attentive reader and informed interpreter of ideology will not forego Destutt de Tracy's identification of sensing with *acting ("sentir une sensation, un souvenir, un rapport, est une action tout comme sentir")* (65, p. 70) .

The importance of this qualification cannot be overemphasized. It definitely deprives sensationalism (at least the Destutt de Tracy version) of one of its heaviest burdens, i.e., the above denounced purely passive and inert character of sensation and thought. It remains true, however, that Destutt de Tracy made no attempt to further describe or define the nature of action he had in mind when he identified sensing with acting. The question was answered many years later when Johannes Müller, reviving and revitalizing Aristotelian views, traced the active component of sensation, more particularly vision, to a power or *dynamics* passing in sensation from its potential to its actual form of existence, in terms of the specific *energies* of the senses. Johannes Müller thereby introduced a metaphysical element (or *entelechia*) in physiology, thus reaffirming, though unwittingly, Galen's concept of living organisms and their "natural faculties." I am not too sure that Pinel would have welcomed this extension and amplification of ideology. In spite of the tribute paid to him by Destutt de Tracy, he did not seem to be a blind follower of ideology. At any rate, he hoped that his observations on the insane might have a favorable influence on the principles of ideology and change its direction.

> Any metaphysical discussion concerning the nature of mania has been eliminated, and I have concentrated only upon the historical exposé of the various disorders of the understanding and the will and on the corresponding physical changes which manifest themselves outwardly by perceptible signs—disorderly movements of the body, incoherences or absurdities in speech, or bizarre and unusual gestures. The history of mental alienation then becomes one of the physical sciences, and it deserves all the more to be the object of serious study since treatment lacking this basis is reduced to dangerous gropings or a blind empiricism (3).

It seems strange that Pinel mentioned in this paragraph his own intention to forego any metaphysical discussion on the nature of mania, thus leading the reader (perhaps unwittingly) to the conclusion that ideology does harbor metaphysical elements. Such a conclusion, however, would not be justified. Destutt de Tracy distinguished between metaphysics as an "art of imagination" and his own science, which rested on observation and the direct witness of the senses as its ultimate sources:

> Locke is, I think, the first who attempted to observe and describe human intelligence as one observes and describes the properties of a mineral or a plant, or a notable instance in the life of an animal; so he made his study a part of physics. It is not that, before him, there had not been many hypotheses advanced on this subject or much audacious dogmatizing on the nature of our soul; but it was always with the purpose, not of discovering the source of our knowledge, its certainty and its limits, but of determining the beginning and the end of everything, of divining the origin and destination of the world. This is the object of metaphysics. We shall classify it among the arts of imagination, designed to satisfy us, not to instruct us (65, Preface, pp. XV and XVI).

The problem involved in the chapter on ideology, called by Destutt de Tracy "On Existence," is that of the existence or denial of objective reality. Pinel could not be expected to delve into the intricacies of a theory of experience. His mind was not set for pure speculation. The observational approach was repeatedly stressed by him: the cure and care of the patient remained his primary concern, and his physical and spiritual eyes were watching the concrete and shocking realities of insane behavior and asylums—all these factors hardly allowed him to go into a theory of knowledge for its own sake. He adopted the philosophic system of Locke and Condillac merely as a precious tool for a better understanding and guidance of his alienated patients. Though observation does not exclude reasoning and theory (it rather implies them), it remains true that in the march of time and medical history, observational science and medicine have repeatedly emerged as antagonistic to the spirit of disappointing "systems" and gratuitous speculations, after these have reached their limits. Still, on one occasion, Pinel declared:

> The writings of Plato, Seneca, and other philosophers of antiquity will be found of greater service in the prevention of insanity than any pharmaceutical formulae of tonics and antispasmodics (3).

As far as I can see this is the only passage in which Pinel referred no longer to cure alone but also to *prevention* of insanity. He called this prevention "an exclusively moral" one, thus applying the same connotation used by him for treatment to prevention of insanity. This was a most courageous and as yet not too well-known step, anticipating developments which reached their climax not until a century later, ultimately to be shaped and organized on a world-wide scale under the guise of mental hygiene. I submit that the "exclusively moral" type of prevention which Pinel had in mind was an *educational* one. It is above all the reference to Seneca which suggests this conclusion. The Stoic's advice to subjugate the passions— "There are no passions so fierce and self-willed that they cannot be subjugated by discipline" (63)—and his conviction that they are states of "temporary madness" read like anticipations of Pinel's view that insanity originates from wild passions and has to be treated accordingly. *It is the education of the passions which emerges as the criterion of moral treatment as well as moral prevention from the writings of both Seneca and Pinel.*

Of greatest significance for the problem of Pinel's indebtedness to sensationalism and its effect on his view on mental alienation is the following passage:

> In mania, at its highest degree of intensity, when the understanding is assailed by a rapid succession of the most incoherent and tumultuous ideas, attention is *completely destroyed,* as well as judgment and the *inner awareness of one's own existence.** The insane, incapable of all reflection about himself, *is unaware of all his relations to external objects.* From his gestures and his utterances we observe in him *ideas other than those which could be produced by impressions upon his sense organs;* and these ideas are without order, are disconnected, and seem to arise automatically, to appear and disappear instantaneously, and to follow their impetuous course like a torrent. I might cite as an example a man whose mental condition I was recently asked to assess. I, as well as two of his relatives for whom he had formerly felt tender affection, asked him different questions in vain: he uttered, without order and without logical sequence, the words *tree, hat, sky,* etc., turning his head away; he then mumbled in a low voice inarticulate sounds; then suddenly raising his voice angrily and fixing his eyes upon the sky, he uttered piercing cries, finally became calm shortly afterwards, without ceasing to speak in the most incoherent manner about imaginary objects (3, pp. 78-79) .

The informed reader cannot overlook in this passage certain expressions reaffirming the basic tenets of Condillac's sensationalism in almost genuine terms. These expressions and their underlying thought evidently serve the purpose of illustrating and supporting Pinel's interpretation and treatment of insane behavior. Small and casual as this passage seems to be, it uncovers the intellectual area where the philosophical systems constructed by Locke and Condillac and the basic tenets of ideology are recognizable as being truly incorporated in Pinel's thought and action. The passage, therefore, is of crucial importance for the historical as well as philosophical evaluation of Pinel's view on mental alienation and his *Traité médico-philosophique.*

In brief, Pinel's decision, reached in a crucial situation, to give up the principles of Locke and Condillac and to invoke the pathogenic and curative power of the will (instead of that of pure under-

---

* Italics are mine (W.R.) .

standing), does not appear to be justified by a closer scrutiny of the texture of these systems, both of which left ample room for will, desire, necessity and freedom. Pinel might have referred with greater justification to Destutt de Tracy, the chief of that school of thought known as ideologists, whose teaching reached Pinel as well as many of the literary and scholarly figures and circles of his time. That Pinel's work was highly appraised by Destutt de Tracy is demonstrated beyond doubt by a footnote in *Ideologie*, which in the English version reads as follows:

> This thought was suggested to me by the reading of the *Traité de l'aliénation mentale* which Pinel published; I cannot recommend too highly the reading of it. In explaining the unreason of the insane, he explores the reasoning of the sane; he proves that *the art of healing the demented is no different from that of handling the passions and directing the opinions of the ordinary man;** it consists in forming their habits. It will be the philosophical physiologists like Pinel who will promote ideology. He not only has the glory of having written a useful book; he has, moreover, that of having gathered the material for it by means of a long sequence of worthy activities. Besides, I have seen with great satisfaction that the phenomena which he describes with great perfection confirm the manner in which I have conceived of thought, and are better explained in relation to ideology, by our way of considering our intellectual faculties, than by those in use up to now.

> Everyone begins with infantile idiocy, ends with senile dementia, and has in the interim a greater or lesser degree of delirious mania, in accordance with the degree of disorder in their most profoundly habitual intellectual operations.

> The moral treatment which Pinel uses to restore confused minds is rightly the precise opposite of the procedures used by the oratorial art to shake man's imagination and enlist his acquiescence (65).

Pinel and L'Encyclopédie

It was only by slow and continuous progress that, beginning with the twelfth century, Greek medicine was known in the University of

* Italics are mine (W.R.).

Paris, and, above all, that it was disseminated and made better known by the aid of the admirable invention of printing towards the end of the fifteenth century. We must pay tribute to the enlightenment and indefatigable zeal which this famous school displayed in gradually preparing for and assuring the reign of observational medicine.* But to judge soundly the spirit of those times when the sciences were reawakening in Europe, we must remember what d'Alembert says on this subject in the preliminary discourse of the *Encyclopédie*:

> The study of languages and of history, abandoned of necessity during the centuries of ignorance, was the first to which man devoted himself. The human mind found itself, upon emerging from barbarism, in a sort of infancy, eager to accumulate ideas, and yet incapable at first of acquiring those of a certain type because of the sort of dullness in which the faculties of the mind had lain for so long. Of all the faculties, memory was the first to be cultivated, because it is the easiest to satisfy; they did not, therefore, begin by studying nature as discoverers should have done. The writings of the ancients began to be commonly known, and they thought they had only to read in order to become learned. So they devoured indiscriminately all that the ancients had handed down to us; they translated them, they wrote commentaries upon them and, through a sort of gratitude, they set about adoring them, without knowing too well what they were worth.

What D'Alembert says of sciences in general applies particularly to Greek medicine. From the sixteenth century on, they studied with extreme ardor the writings of the Greek physicians, of which correct editions had just been published in Venice, Rome, and Paris. A host of editors, commentators, and scholiasts cited passages from Hippocrates and Galen as from so many oracles and tormented themselves night and day to explain the obscure meaning of a Greek term or to reconcile contradictory texts. The most distinguished, such as Mercuriales, Prosper Martianus, Duretus, Balonius, Hollerius, etc., devoted themselves to the observation of diseases only in order to grasp better the true meaning of the Greek authors, but hardly with the intention of rectifying them or of extending by new investigations the field of observation. It was Galenism especially which was

---

* Notice des hommes les plus célèbres de la Faculté de Médecine en l'Université de Paris, depuis 1110 jusqu'a 1750, etc., par Jacques-Albert Hazon, Paris.

disastrous to the schools and which encouraged the violent diatribes of the followers of Paracelsus or of what is called the sect of chemists, which pledged, so to speak, the destruction of Greek medicine, but which could offer in opposition only the absurdities of a false chemistry (2, pp. LXXIX-LXXX).

But to trace vestiges of Pinel's view on mental alienation to the *Encyclopédie* would be a hopeless undertaking, since this view was still far from being obtained by the eminent alienist at the time of the first (1751) and the second (1777) edition of the *Encyclopédie*. It is most revealing to compare the formulation of our subject (mania) as it appeared in the *Encyclopédie* with that reached by Pinel in his treatise on mental alienation. The author of the article "Mania" in the *Encyclopédie* was Ménuret de Chambaud, of whom we learn that he was physician to Dumouriez, a French general with whom he defected to the enemy; Ménuret died in Hamburg and left a medical monograph on that city (21c, p. 167).

It is true that Ménuret discussed in his article, though in a cursory manner, the symptomatology, the then (as today) still unknown etiology, the (rather vague and inconclusive) cerebral pathology, the differential diagnosis, and the unsystematic and purely physical therapy of mania; but he did not even mention psychotherapeutical procedures, though they had been in existence since the days of the ancients. *The reader passing from Ménuret's article to Pinel's treatise on mental alienation and, more particularly, to his "moral treatment" does not gain the impression of passing from one author to another contemporary one, but rather from one age to another*; the endeavor of Pinel stands out as an accomplishment breaking suddenly with the tradition and routine of his own era. I am inclined to believe that it was *Pinel's growing concept of moral treatment which proved to be a cooperative factor in his acceptance of the faculties of the human mind as a principle of classification of insanity*. No matter whether he approached his subject as a natural historian, a clinician, a diagnostician, a therapist or a superintendent: *he always approached the mentally disturbed individual in his own terms*, i.e., those of mentality. This, I submit, was his Cartesian heritage; even a shadow of Spinozism might have fallen on him, since he did not only do justice to the strictness of the Cartesian distinction between mind and body but also to the obligation derived from the teaching of Spinoza (who was very popular in the early eighteenth century) that each of the two parallel series, i.e., the psychical and the physical ones, remain isolated from one another and must be expressed in its own terms, but never the one in terms of the other.

Pinel was not the first author to attempt a *classification of mental derangements*. But he did not want to discuss "the arbitrary distributions of nosologists, as in most instances they are far from being the result of accurate observation and experience" (4, p. 134). His principle of classification was intended *to divide "a disease affecting primarily or secondarily the faculties of the human mind"* (4, p. 135).

> I do not wish in any way to write a satire but to describe the true story of a very real disease: I must therefore discard the popular meaning of *delirium, craze, confusion, insanity,* as well as all metaphysical discussions, all theories concerning the nature of intellectual or emotional functions and their genesis, their order, their reciprocal concatenation, their sequence. *I rely entirely upon observation, from which we learn the unsuspected truth that there can be a disorder limited to the perceptual sphere, to memory, to imagination, to judgment, to awareness of one's own existence, to volitional impulses, and that the combination of any number of these disorders having various degrees of intensity constitutes an infinity of types. It is all the more essential to stress these fundamental objects and to suggest their special study, should we wish to proceed more systematically in our observation of the phenomena of insanity, apply more successfully to this disease the analytical method, and promote further progress in history** (3, pp. 4-5).

He thus designed the following scheme:

> The powers of perception and imagination are frequently disturbed without any excitement of the passions. The functions of the understanding, on the other hand, are often perfectly sound, while the man is driven by his passions to acts of turbulence and outrage. In many lunatics, a periodical or continued delirium are united to extravagance and fury. Again, instances are not unfrequent of actual dementia or mental disorganization, where the ideas and internal emotions appear to have no connection with the impressions of sense, and to succeed each other without order, and to vanish without leaving any traces of their existence. A still more deplorable condition is that of a total obliteration of the thinking faculties,

---

* Italics are mine (W.R.).

"Q" or a privation more or less absolute of all ideas and emotions: in other words, a state of complete idiotism (4).

. . . The older nosologists, Sauvages, Sagar, and Linnaeus, were not wholly unaware of these distinctions, for in their distributions of mental disorders we find, besides an order of *Vesaniae* or *Hallucinations,* in which erroneous impressions were supposed to affect the understanding, another department styled *Morositates,* or *Morbi Pathetici,* consisting of depraved appetites and other morbid changes in the feelings and propensities. The disordered states, however, which are classed under these heads are not all strictly forms of insanity: And *Pinel* appears to have been the *first* writer who, *with a clear conception on the subject, distinguished a class of mental disorders under the term* of *"madness without delirium"* (4).

. . . 1. Moral *insanity,* or madness consisting in a morbid perversion of the natural feelings, affections, inclinations, temper, habits, moral dispositions, and natural impulses, without any remarkable disorder or defect of the intellect or knowing and reasoning faculties, and particularly without any insane illusion or hallucination.

The three following modifications of the disease may be termed *intellectual insanity* in contradistinction to the preceding form.

2. *Monomania,* or partial insanity, in which the understanding is partially disordered or under the influence of some particular illusion, referring to one subject, and involving one train of ideas, while the intellectual powers appear, when exercised on other subjects, to be in a great measure unimpaired.

3. *Mania,* or raving madness, in which the understanding is generally deranged; the reasoning faculty, if not lost, is confused and disturbed in its exercise; the mind is in a state of morbid excitement, and the individual talks absurdly on every subject to which his thoughts are momentarily directed.

4. *Incoherence,* or dementia. By some persons it may be thought scarcely correct to term this a form of insanity, as it has been generally considered a result and sequel of that disease. In some instances, however, mental derangement has nearly this character from the commencement, or at least assumes it at a very early period. I am therefore justified in stating it, after Pinel, to

"Q" be a fourth and distinct form of madness. It is thus characterized
by that justly celebrated writer: "Rapid succession of uninterrupted alternation of insulated ideas, and evanescent and unconnected emotions; continually repeated acts of extravagance;
complete forgetfulness of every previous state; diminished sensibility to external impressions; abolition of the faculty of judgment; perpetual activity. . . ."

The division of the forms of insanity pointed out in the preceding chapter is the most simple that is admissible, or adaptable
to the existing varieties of disease; it is entirely practical, and
founded on observation. A more extensive arrangement has
been laid down by Professor Heinroth in his celebrated *Treatise on Derangement of the Mental Faculties,* a work which,
though singular and absurd in some of its fundamental principles, is perhaps, of all treatises on disorders of the mind, the
most elaborate and comprehensive. Heinroth's distribution is
theoretical or speculative rather than the result of actual observation and experience; yet it will be found worthy of consideration.

The disorders of the mind, according to that writer, are only
limited in number and in kind by the diversities which exist in
the operations. They are of three distinct kinds, and are referred
on the testimony of consciousness to three different departments
in our inward nature, viz., to those on the feeling or sentiment
(*des Gemüths*), the understanding, and the will. The emotions
of joy, grief, pleasure, and pain, the mental processes of reflection and contemplation, and the voluntary act of self-determina-
tion, are three kinds of mental phenomena, which, as they
present themselves to our inward consciousness, are so clearly
and strongly distinguished from each other that it is impossible
to confound them. "If the cause of derangement is in relation
to one of these manifestations of mental existence—and to one
or another it must belong, since the mind is ever occupied with
phenomena related to one out of the three classes—we have only
to inquire as to which modification the disorder actually refers
itself, or whether it affects the feelings, the understanding, or
the will. Since one of these has possession of our consciousness,
or is at least predominant at every point of time, whichever
function of the mind happens to be that which is falling into
disorder, by it the form of insanity is determined." Thus we
have, continues Heinroth, three classes of mental diseases cor-

responding to the three departments of our minds. A second
distinction is founded on the character of the disturbance
which is experienced; whether it is of the nature of exaltation
or depression, of increased or diminished excitement. . . . (35a,
p. 169).

In Pinel's day mental alienation had still to struggle for a technical *name* of its own. It is precisely by classification that human
understanding secures to a given species its place and its name, i.e.,
its diagnosis; classification, diagnosis, and definition being but three
aspects of the same reasoning or working of intellect. In Ménuret's
article on mania, the term is used synonymously with delirium—a
delirium of "universal" nature and without fever, but with audacity
and anger. It is used synonymously with madness (*folie*) or imbecility when the individual affected remains gentle, calm, or simply
"ridiculous." After all, these terms were understood by our author
merely to be degrees or species of mania determined by the same
cause, all these terms covering diseases of long duration, in which
the patients not only rave, but have wrong perceptions and act sense-
lessly. When their delirium is restricted to one or two objects, with
their behavior otherwise remaining normal, they are termed melancholics. We witness classification at its birth, still undecided and not
yet isolating one species from another. In this respect, it is significant
that the first edition of Pinel's treatise bears the title: *Traité médico-
philosophique sur l'aliénation mentale ou la manie*. Thus the name
"manie" was still used by Pinel as *pars pro toto*, or synonymous
with mental alienation. Under the circumstances, to search for a
definition of mania would mean to search for a definition of mental
alienation.

Pinel on Observation

"Q" We see that we must adopt as a guide in medicine the method
which constantly succeeds in all fields of natural history, which
is to say that we must begin by looking attentively at each
object in succession with no other intention than to assemble
material for the future; that we must attempt, in short, to avoid
all illusion, all preconception, all opinion adopted by hearsay.
This is exactly what I have done over a long period of years
with regard to mental alienation, not only in private institutions

but also successively in the great asylums of Bicêtre and
Salpétrière (3, p. 3).

Observation and Experimentation

The Passive Aspect of Ideology: The author who prepared the
article, "History of Psychology," for the 1955 edition (Volume 18)
of the *Encyclopedia Britannica* presumes that Condillac continued
the French mechanistic tradition inaugurated by Descartes. Our
author considers the history of reflex action as "basic to the mechanistic conception of mind," which he dates from Descartes. But at the
end of my own analysis of Descartes' ideas of brain function (37) I
raised the question, "What finally remains of the famous mechanistic
view of life for which Descartes had been held responsible for 300
years?" Be this as it may, neither the term nor the concept of reflex
action occurs in Condillac's writings, which do not reveal any vestiges of their author's inclination or claim to deal with physiological
problems. The term "reflex" is not even listed in Condillac's *Dictionnaire des Synonymes*. Destutt de Tracy, though considering Condillac as the founder of ideology, confessed at the end of his *Eléments
d'Idéologie* that he (Destutt de Tracy) regretfully neglected the
physiological implications of ideology due to the limitations of his
project and those of his knowledge, but that he expects the physiological philosophers, and above all Cabanis, to fill in these gaps in
ideology. However, he had nothing to say about any physiological
contributions made by Condillac.

One might argue that the mechanical nature of Condillac's psychology, though not just resting on reflex action, has other creden-
tials, such as, for instance, the association of ideas of which Condillac
indeed made ample use.

Moral Treatment as a Department of Observational Medicine:
Destutt de Tracy's identification of sensing with acting *("sentir . . .
est une action")*, though dissatisfying to the reader demanding the
rationale of this identification, i.e., the explanation of the nature of
the "action" in question, does not indicate that the concept of moral
treatment is incompatible with ideology. Indeed, as long as ideology
affirms a purely passive sensationalism, no room is left for a treatment
which calls for the very active types of behavior, the decisions, and
above all, the responsibility of the patient who in moral treatment
remains the permanent target of educational measures. But as soon

as an activating component is granted to ideology and its four elements—sensibility, memory, desire, and judgment—*moral treatment* may be considered, as Pinel considered it, a *department of observational* medicine. Thus it preserved the whole of Pinel's thought and action, the spirit and the letter of Hippocratic medicine, which ever since the days of the Greeks has been described, defined, and appraised as observational medicine. It seems that it was left to the eighteenth century to justify and, above all, to amplify this qualification, precisely by *depriving the observational component of its alleged passive aspect* and by granting to it *an active and thus a therapeutical aspect* which then allowed Pinel to *include his moral treatment in observational medicine*, strange and provocative as this inclusion at first seems to be.

Pinel's endeavor thus *emerges not only as a revival of Hippocratic medicine but, above all, as its logical continuation and climax.* Thus would be silenced the objection repeatedly raised to Hippocratic or observational medicine as being fatalistic. *Thus also comes to an end the paralyzing dialectics between a purely observational, expectant treatment and experimental, aggressive treatment.* I see in Pinel's implicit solution of this dialectics one of his major if not his greatest contribution to thought in medicine and its liberating effect.

There are, of course, passages in Pinel's treatise revealing the traditional passive attitude of the observational physician. "In this disease (mania) as in many others," he said, "nature tries to cure and to reestablish the regularity of the functions of understanding." "All that is needed," he continued, "is to remain faithful to the general laws of hygiene, to strengthen the conservative tendencies, and to give them the time to develop" (3, p. 341). Repeatedly, he refers to the *vis medicatrix naturae* and the Stahlian "principle of conservation, whose office it is to repel any attack upon the system injurious to its well-being, or fatal to its existence" (4, p. 40). In this connection he ventured the hypothesis that in unfortunate cases the general and salutary laws of the *vis conservatrix* were impeded in their action by some organic lesion of the nervous system (4, p. 41). Though the informed reader is prepared to include Stahl's "principle of conservation" in a purely observational and expectant scheme of medical thought and action, Pinel's reference to the Stahlian principle still remains surprising in the light of his own denunciation, in the introduction to *Traité médico-philosophique sur l'aliénation mentale*, of Stahl and "the somber rays of his profound and enigmatic doctrine." But there are at least three instances in which the moral treatment can be proved to be rooted in purely observational thought. In view of the fundamental importance of the problem at stake, the history of the first case has been translated (for the first time) and is reported in extenso:

"Q" A man in the prime of life, confined to Bicêtre, believes himself to be a king and expresses himself always in a tone of command and of supreme authority. He had undergone the ordinary treatment at the Hôtel-Dieu, where blows and acts of violence on the part of the attendants had served only to make him more enraged and more dangerous. How should one handle him? Imposing devices for restraint could embitter him still more, and humoring him would confirm his fantastic pretensions. It was necessary, therefore, to await a favorable opportunity to get hold of such a difficult character, and here is the one that chance provided. One day, this insane patient wrote to his wife a letter full of anger and bitterly accused her of prolonging his detention in order to enjoy complete liberty; he threatened her, besides, with all the force of his vengeance. Before sending this letter, he read it to another patient, who was convalescent; he disapproved of these furiously angry expressions and reproached him in a friendly tone for attempting to reduce his wife to despair. This wise advice was listened to and accepted. The letter was not sent and was replaced with another full of moderation and regard. The supervisor of the asylum, informed of this amenability to friendly remonstrances, saw obvious signs of a favorable change to come, and he hastened to take advantage of it. He went to the patient's cell to talk to him and gradually brought him back to the principal object of his delirium. "If you are the sovereign," he said to him, "why do you not put an end to your detention, and why do you remain in the midst of insane people of all sorts?" He returned on the following day to reason with him in this way, adopting a tone of benevolence and friendship: he showed him little by little the ridiculousness of his exaggerated pretensions, pointing out to him another patient who had long been convinced that he was endowed with supreme power and had become an object of derision. The maniac was at first shaken, soon began to doubt his sovereign title, and finally came to recognize his fantastic aberrations. It was in a fortnight that this so unexpected psychological revolution (*révolution morale*) was achieved, and after some months of probation this respectable father was returned to his family (3, pp. 254-256).

"Q" A literary gentleman, who was given to the pleasures of the table, and who was lately recovered from a tertian fever, experienced in the season of autumn all the horrors of the propensity to suicide. He weighed with shocking calmness the choice of various methods to accomplish the deed of death. A visit which he paid to London appears to have developed with a new degree of energy his profound melancholy and his immovable resolution to abridge his term of life. He chose an advanced hour of the night, and went towards one of the bridges of that capital for the purpose of precipitating himself into the Thames. But at the moment of his arrival at the destined spot, he was attacked by robbers. Though he had little or no money about him, he felt extremely indignant at this treatment, and used every effort to make his escape; which, however, he did not accomplish before he had been exceedingly terrified. Left by his assailants, he returned to his lodgings, having forgot the original object of his sally. This encounter seems to have operated a thorough revolution in the state of his mind. His cure was so complete that, though he has since been a resident of Paris for ten years, and has subsisted frequently upon scanty and precarious resources, he has not been since tormented by disgust with life. This is a case of melancholic vesania, which yielded to the sudden and unforeseen impression of terror (4, pp. 232-233).

I shall add another case of melancholia, accompanied by a propensity to suicide, which yielded to a remedy of an analogous nature. It is that of a watchmaker, who was for a long time harassed by the propensity in question. He once so far gave way to the horrid impulse that he withdrew to his house in the country, where he expected to meet no obstacle to the execution of his project. Here he one day took a pistol and retired to an adjoining wood, with the full intent of perpetrating the fatal deed, but missing his aim, the contents of the piece entered his cheek. Violent hemorrhage ensued. He was discovered and conveyed to his own house. During the healing of the wound, which was long protracted, an important change took place in the state of his mind. Whether from the agitation produced by the tragic attempt, from the enormous loss of blood which it occasioned, or from any other cause, he never afterwards showed the least inclination to put an end to his existence. This case, though by no means an example for imitation, is well-calculated to show

that sudden terror or any other lively or deep impression may
divert and even destroy the fatal propensity to suicide (4, pp.
233-234).

Still another case is that of *melancholia vesania* which yielded
to the sudden and unforeseen impression of terror. Pinel added a
case which he believed to be "well-calculated to show that sudden
terror or any other lively or deep impression may divert and even
destroy the fatal propensity to suicide" (4, p. 234).

In brief, a "favorable circumstance" or a terrifying encounter
emerges as the crucial terms from these case histories when looked
upon as examples of moral treatment rooted in observational
thought. In other words, it is not by the physician's active and aggressive intervention but by mere chance that a change in the patient's
thought and behavior, leading ultimately to his recovery, comes into
being. The *spontaneous* occurrence of a "favorable circumstance"
or a "sudden terror" can be considered to be within the realm and
the limits of pure observation, which thus remains the framework
within which the therapeutical change becomes noticeable. A return
of the same or an analogous "favorable circumstance" is likely to have
the same strengthening effect as an experiment repeated at will and
intended to demonstrate with greater strength to the experimenter
the determinism of a given vital phenomenon. Thus Pinel's thesis
that repeated observation is a source of moral treatment indeed
seems justified.

Senses as instruments: The difference between observation and
experimentation ceases to be a fundamental one as soon as we grant
to the senses the same role as devices or tools which we ascribe to
the experimental equipment. *The senses then emerge as a great complex of vital devices destined to bring a changing world into the orbit
of man's observational power. Man himself then emerges as a permanent experimenter carrying his vital equipment with him every-
where; but never being indebted to any foreign and inert device
which, though he constructed it himself, always threatens to enslave
him.* This conclusion may be used to *silence the argument that experimentation is an artifact isolating the experimental subject from
life and undisturbed nature.* By our conclusion, *experimentation is
brought into the orbit of the natural conditions and spontaneity of
life.* Animate nature, when studied under experimental conditions,
appears no longer in distress and under torture.

It is the determinism of vital phenomena or causal thought which
emerges from this comparative analysis of observational and experi-

mental reasonings as common to both the observer and experimenter. Both want to understand and, if possible, to master vital phenomena by tracing them to those agents which determined the appearance of these phenomena. In observation the result is, as a rule, embedded in an often confusing whole of circumstances and conditions which makes it difficult to identify just that condition which acts as the adequate or essential cause of the observational result. In experimentation, however, the tendency is to narrow the margin of causative agents and, if ever possible, to seize one single factor as the truly decisive one in the complex of associate, cooperative, or precipitating conditions. This tendency, if successful, is at the root of experimental therapy of any type with which an observationally conceived treatment may not be able to compete. On the other hand, the latter will always be closer to an unprovoked nature and to the spontaneity of its manifestations, while experimentation can never deny its artificial character, which isolates experimentation and experimenter from the flow of undisturbed and uninterrupted life phenomena. In a sense, experimentation is superior to observation, since it offers a body of coherent results which allow man to cure or to prevent diseases. But in another sense, observation is superior to experimentation, since it leaves to man a greater freedom of action and lesser dependence on self-constructed tools and technical devices.

Pinel's Debt to Sensationalism

Pinel's debt to sensationalism can be derived from the following passage:

> In order to trace knowledge upon the subject of perception analytically, and to arrive at its sources, Condillac supposes an animated statue which he endows successively with the functions of smell, taste, hearing, sight, and touch, and refers to each its appropriate impressions and ideas. It cannot be doubted that to consider the faculties of the mind separately would facilitate the study of pneumatology as well as lead to very important knowledge in regard to the nature and varieties of insanity (4).

It was unquestionably Condillac's intention to study our senses separately, to distinguish precisely what ideas we owe to each sense, to observe how the senses are trained and how one sense aids another.

It still remains to be seen whether or not Pinel's freely admitted debt to sensationalism and its apologist Condillac would justify the conclusion that Pinel adhered to that theory of experience which regards the latter as the *only* source of knowledge. The question has never been raised before, though Pinel's emphasis on observational and experimental thought should have suggested this investigation. But the truth is that Pinel's work has never been analyzed as to its epistemological constituents. As stressed repeatedly in my own studies and again in the present investigation, it has been the interest in Pinel's humanitarian figure and achievements which, from the outset, overshadowed the interest in Pinel's medical thought and medical philosophy. We have to go back to the sources, i.e., to Pinel's own utterances and confessions and their historical roots and ramifications, in order to uncover the scaffolding on which Pinel's reasoning power and trained understanding constructed his superior interpretation of mental alienation and its treatment according to insight and plan (though always assisted by moral virtues). We have reason to believe that Pinel was familiar with that division of man's virtues which is Aristotelian in origin. The division sheds light on the powerful influence to which Pinel's courage, intrepidity, fearlessness, and his other *moral virtues* were subjected by his *intellectual virtues,* such as prudence, foresight, tenacity, and his sense of strategy and tactic.

In our attempt to answer the question raised as to whether or not Pinel's thought was a strictly empirical one, we can be assisted by Deichgräber's (18) analysis of the doctrine and the teaching of the Greek medical school which carries this name. Its extant fragments were collected and interpreted by Deichgräber. It is, above all, the use of observations made by others, the imitation of a conscious or unconscious experience, the constant use of *recollection* and *repetition*—in brief, it is *tradition* and *routine* which emerges from Deichgräber's analysis as the lifeline of the doctrine and the teaching of that school of medical thought which was to be one of the three medical sects of the ancients claiming and perpetuating *previous experiences* handed down to posterity as the sole criterion of knowledge. The mind of the empiricist thus appears as a *passive* rather than an active one, his science as the sum total of repeated observations which do not form a well-organized and systematically constructed body of knowledge. Nevertheless, the empiricists strove also for criteria of the usefulness of traditional data.

There could hardly be a greater contrast than that between these significant tenets of the empiricists cited by Deichgräber and the principles of Pinel's interpretation and treatment of mental alienation. Pinel's mind was an active one, dissatisfied with recollection and repetition, exploring rather *new* methods and liquidating paralyzing traditions. He stands out in the history of medicine and civilization as a *renovator* but not as a follower, as a trustee to one of man's hopes rather than as a curator of man's sorrows and failures. No better testimonial for this conclusion could be found than his own confession expressed by the following question: "Could a physician, treading slavishly the beaten paths, lacking sound judgment and an ardent desire for knowledge, be fully aware and conscious of the true significance of the endless observations he will make?" (3, pp. X-XI).

Pinel's Theory and Practice of Mental Treatment

Physical Treatment of Mental Disorders

It is neither possible nor necessary to enumerate all *physical treatments of mental disorders* ever conceived by physicians of the past. It seems that almost no organ was omitted as the presumable source of insanity. The brain, however, did not emerge until the nineteenth century as the responsible source of mental alienation. The sixteenth century physician Paracelsus may be mentioned, since he introduced chemical concepts for the first time, though very crude and speculative ones that cannot be projected on modern concepts of biochemistry, and that did not deny their origin from alchemy. He distinguished (for the cure) two kinds of *mania,* one caused by *distillation,* the other by *sublimation.* Mania was believed by him to "rise" from the extremities—the stomach, the liver, the lungs, the intestines, and the kidneys—with distillation and sublimation taking place in one or the other of these organs; but the finer mechanisms of these processes and the rising distilled humors remain unintelligible to an uninformed twentieth-century reader. Moreover, the whole design carries *vitalistic* entities, such as the *spiritus vitae* as a factor participating in the genesis of mania. According to Paracelsus, there are two *remedies* which remove mania, one *surgical* and the other *physical.* The surgical remedy consists of opening or ulcerating the skin at the place from which mania rises. Two phases of the physical treatment of mania are distinguished; one that cools off and congeals the noxious matter of mania, the other which soothes and kills the matter from which mania is born. Camphor, mandragore, papaverine, hyoscyamine, and antimony are listed among the powerful medicines

166

removing mania, some of them, such as camphor, "in a miraculous way."

Pinel on Cerebral Pathology in Mental Alienation

An author who, like Pinel, adopts the faculties of the human *mind* as a principle of classification, who believes the human *passions* to be the true causes of insanity, and who designs its *"moral"* treatment, is not likely to favor a *physical concept of mental alienation*. We must admire the objectivity of the author of *A Treatise On Insanity*, who, in spite of his all too obvious predilection for the study, classification, and therapy of "mania" in its own (i.e., mental) terms, did not neglect to discuss the factual evidences available at his time and their interpretations favoring or not favoring a physical genesis of mental alienation. Certain observations taught him indeed to presume that the primary "seat" of periodical mania is almost always in the epigastric region. But he continued by stating, ". . . that from this center are propagated, as it were by a species of irradiation, the accessions of insanity." He thus believed the latter to be a remote effect, by sympathy or consensus (terms or concepts which he undoubtedly had on his mind when making this qualifying statement), and which he owed to an age-old tradition of medical thought and medical history. A century later, they reappeared under the guise of *actions at a distance* in the terminology of Brown-Séquard, a most eminent experimental physiologist, and under the guise of *diaschisis* in the terminology of C. von Monakow, one of the greatest continental neurologists of the nineteenth and twentieth centuries. Pinel's "species of irradiation" gains its historical significance as a preconcept of these two later versions of sympathy or consensus (50). The initial disorder suspected by Pinel to be in the primary seat, i.e., the epigastric region, must be expected to reach the brain by "irradiation"; thus originated the problem of a *cerebral pathology of insanity*. Again, Pinel proved to be of greatest *"circumspection and reserve in deciding upon the physical causes of mental alienation."*

The anatomy and pathology of the brain are yet involved in extreme obscurity. Greding dissected two hundred and sixteen maniacal subjects, and he details all the peculiarities which he observed in the meninges, the substance of the brain, the ventricles, the pineal gland, and the cerebellum. But as those maniacs died by disorders unconnected with their mental ailments, we can form no just conclusions from the morbid appearances which presented themselves. Many varieties of structure might likewise accidentally coexist with the lesions of the mental functions, without having any immediate connection with them. The same may be said of the experiments of a similar nature by Haslam in England, and Chiarugi in Italy. I have attended at thirty-six dissections in the Bicêtre hospital; and I can declare that I have never met with any other appearance within the cavity of the cranium than are observable on opening the bodies of persons who have died of apoplexy, epilepsy, nervous fevers, and convulsions. From such data, what light can be thrown on the subject of insanity? (4, pp. 132-133).

He reserved for another occasion the exposition and details of his own anatomical researches in regard to insanity. I was unable to trace this investigation. Again, one cannot expect the inaugurator of moral treatment to be too enthusiastic about a therapy of insanity by physical means. In this respect, it is significant that precisely when discussing the subject, Pinel reaffirmed his own thesis with unusual clearness and emphasis:

Attaching as I do little importance to pharmaceutic preparations, and great importance, in curable cases, to physical and moral regimen, I intend not to devote many of my pages to the exclusive consideration of drugs and medicaments. My objects more especially are: to give due importance to the history of mental derangement; to discriminate accurately between the different species of the disease, so as to avoid fortuitous and ineffective treatment; to furnish precise rules for the internal police and government of charitable establishments and asylums; to urge the necessity of providing for the insulation of the different classes of insane patients at houses intended for their confinement; and to place first, in point of consequence, the duties of a humane and enlightened superintendency, and the maintenance of order in the services of hospitals. The remedies which I prescribe are simple, and such as have been ratified by experience. I have endeavored to attend to the stages and species of the disorder most adapted for medical treatment, and most promising of success. I reserve for extreme cases, and such as hold out little prospect of a cure, the employment of certain active remedies, which, in other circumstances, I should consider either as unnecessary or dangerous (4, pp. 221-222).

Again, when exhibiting and interpreting his general table of cases of insanity cured at the Bicêtre Asylum by regimen and exercise exclusively, more particularly, by repeated bleeding and the cold bath, he felt the need for making the concluding remark:

> It is equally obvious, and to be lamented, that unhappy dispositions and violent passions are the most ordinary causes of insanity. Another truth not less important, and evident on a view of the above table, and which directly tends to impose restrictions upon the prescription of medicaments, is, that the most turbulent and furious madmen, when their disease is periodical, and when their paroxysms correspond with the changes of the seasons, are in general most perfectly and permanently cured. Their restoration is best accomplished by regimen alone: an expedition to Antycira will not in general be found necessary. . . . It is in periodical mania . . . which has hitherto been considered as incurable, and which has commonly terminated in premature death, that medicine should avail herself of her most powerful resources (4, p. 242 and p. 236).

Pinel did not scrutinize the epistemological process which I called for to make intelligible the effect of physical agents on mentality, disturbed or not. It is for this reason that he was free from intellectual scruples when "combining skillfully the resources of moral and physical regimen, so as gradually to induce a favorable change in the character of chronic ailments, and in assisting nature in her efforts to restore the disordered frame to its pristine health and vigor (4). It is this writer's opinion and experience that the combination of the resources of moral and physical regimens may throw into a state of confusion a patient taught to assume the *responsibility* for his conduct, which simultaneously is left to the action of drugs and other physical agents. And how can the therapist himself discriminate between the two agents and thus determine the true road to cure and insight?

Pinel on Classifications

The *classification of the various types of mental alienation* would not constitute a major part of a treatise devoted to the study and rescue of Pinel's *thought*; for that matter, his classification is of the simplest and comprises but four species: 1) melancholia, or delirium with regard to one thing, but without furor, 2) maniacal non-delirious furor, 3) maniacal delirium with extravagant or violent behavior and 4) dementia with abolition of thought. Pinel's classification could not survive, and I leave it to the contemporary clinical psychiatrist to project these terms upon those of present classifications and to save the ideas and the terms which have been able to withstand the tests of time and place. But what matters is that we should know the idea which is the basis for the classifications established by Pinel, the principles of these classifications, and their aim.

As for the principles, it is not difficult to recognize them as the ones adopted by Diderot and d'Alembert in their division of human knowledge, a division borrowed in turn from that established by Bacon upon the various faculties of the human mind.

The fundamental concept which dominates all the other elements of a classification is that of *species*. Now, according to Pinel, species is "a complex idea which combines by abstraction the characteristic features of a disease, selected either from the nature of the exciting causes or from the disorders which are peculiar to it." And Pinel goes on to say that "orders are formed by a new abstraction from characteristics common to different genera, and, similarly, classes from the bringing together of orders." These definitions reveal the most remarkable faculty of their author, that of passing from the various concrete signs manifested by the *patient* to the abstract idea which is his disease. The concept of the disease owes its origin to the understanding and abstract thought of the physician as well as to the perceptible condition of the patient. The passage quoted reveals etiology (the nature of the exciting causes) as well as symptomatology (the nature of the disorders) as principles of classification.

> This classification, aside from its advantage in bringing order and clarity to thinking, becomes very important in the distribution of the mentally ill within the hospitals, the determination of rules of internal discipline, and especially in the establishment of true principles of treatment, which must necessarily be adapted to the nature of each species if one wishes to avoid purely empirical trials (5a, p. 26) .

So much for the structure, the principles, and the aim of the classification of mental alienation into different species. We should not, however, consider these species as rigid entities in conformity with an ontological interpretation of disease.

It would be a mistake to believe that the different species of mania depend on the specific nature of their causes. The different species of mental alienation do not remain invariably the same; that is to say, that a type of mental alienation classified as one species may undergo a sort of transformation during the course of a lifetime and come to be classified as another species (5a, p. 25).

By this judicious observation Pinel succeeds in considering classifications as a function of time; in short, to grant them a chronological and flexible nature. On the other hand we must ask ourselves whether the establishment of true principles of treatment in accordance with classification—thus in accordance with diagnosis—as claimed by Pinel, is still practicable if the species are recognized as being subject to transformations. There would result a continuous transformation of this establishment of true principles of treatment—a result obviously contradictory. It would be better to abandon diagnosis as a principle of treatment and base the latter upon etiology and the past and present condition of the patient, whatever the species referred to at the moment when a therapeutic plan must be established.

In fact, Pinel himself did not follow this therapeutical advice. After having traced the general course followed by irregular periodic mania, he adds:

We notice in the asylums another periodic mania, which is regular, not at all subject to the vicissitudes of the season or to the various other causes which have just been mentioned, but characterized by attacks which are repeated at regular intervals . . . a mania far less easy to cure than the other (5a, p. 32).

But Pinel, in order to explain the fact that "this other mania" is much less easy to cure, does not simply place this variation in another division of his classification, which would in itself suggest a different therapeutic indication; he refers us to "an internal disposition which is known to us only by its effects." Moreover, in the same passage he raises doubts concerning the concepts of madness presented by Locke and Condillac, his own masters in matters philosophical. They considered it exclusively a disposition to combine ideas which are incompatible by nature and to take the ideas thus combined for actual truth (5, p. 32).

Thus Pinel, in his classification, has used certain abstract terms, of which *species* represents the most significant and the most frequently used. It remains true, nevertheless, that the separate species are comprised in the broader concept of mental alienation. So the term *mania* indicates more specifically a general delirium with more or less agitation or a state of furor. Similarly, delirium on one thing exclusively or on a particular group of things is given the name of *melancholia,* whatever variations it may display. The terms *dementia* and *idiocy* are distinguished by other specific characteristics: in *dementia* by a general weakness attacking the intellectual and affective functions, and in *idiocy* by obliteration of reason with rapid and spontaneous episodes of violence (3, p. 6). In his effort to establish a classification based upon exact and judicious observations, suitable for revealing the nature and the signs of diseases, Pinel remained faithful to the rule that he had adopted in his nosography (2a, p. XV) :

> . . . to arrange them in a simple and clear way, beginning with those that are simplest . . ., to rise afterwards to those which are more complex.

Now, there is no doubt that Pinel, well aware of the principal rules of the Cartesian method, was applying the second of them: ". . . to divide . . . of the difficulties . . . into as many parts as may be required for its adequate solution (19, *Discourse on Method,* Part II, p. 129).

Classifications reflect the effort to impose system and order upon the innumerable variations of vital phenomena.* They indicate, thus, an economy of thought, which otherwise would be compelled to start again with each species. They indicate at the same time the effort and the success of generalizing thought, as opposed to the individualizing thought, which is implied in the lowest division of classification and which determines at the same time the end of classification. In spite of the dangers and the weaknesses inherent in

---

* Here indeed is the most critical point in any classification. *Where is the limit beyond which no division should be extended?* The problem seemed already to have been present to the mind of Hippocrates who, in spite of his strong tendency towards individualization, nevertheless did not want to establish an unlimited number of species (nor did he want to renounce the species) . In his polemic remarks against "The Cnidian Sentences" (*On Regimen in Acute Diseases*) he unmistakably rejected their classifying principle: ". . . for their species would be almost innumerable if every symptom experienced by the patients were held to constitute a disease and receive a different name." This disapproval of the Cnidian procedure is preceded by a disapproval of a treatment by admitting of endless varieties of diseases: ". . . Sauvage's nosology can be considered as a revival of the Cnidian principle of classification according to individual symptoms."

classifications, the ancients (i.e., Plato) considered classification to be of divine origin. The reader of Pinel's *Traité médico-philosophique sur l'aliénation mentale* can hardly escape the power of the individualizing thought of its author, who never wearies of reporting the apparently insignificant details of the biographies of his patients. So Pinel, once more, obeys the Hippocratic tradition which demands the observation and retention of all details, even those which may seem insignificant at the very first moment of their observation. But despite the power of his individualizing thought, Pinel always respected the power of generalizing thought as it is affirmed in classifications. We do not find in him the alternative so characteristic of certain twentieth-century authors who advocate and apply individualizing thought to the exclusion of and at the expense of generalizing thought. Basically, it is merely a question of dialectics, thesis and antithesis claiming their rights according to circumstances and need. In this respect, one cannot underestimate the development of thought which led Pinel to "indicate the place which any disease must occupy in a nosographic framework" (1a, p. 6). On this occasion, he pronounces the following sentence so rich in consequences:

> I merely propose, to the man who is eager for sound instruction, the general working of the human mind (1a, p. 9).

In his introduction to *La médecine clinique*, he had already maintained that "diseases . . . studied in relation to their affinities, form a natural chain of ideas, are classified according to their external signs as are all other subjects of natural history, and, finally, are subject to exact and invariable denominations" (1a, p. IX). These details—age, sex, occupation, origin, country in which the disease occurs, place of residence—sometimes impose upon observations a literary rather than scientific character. They recall that derogatory opinion against which Freud had to defend himself by saying that it was neither his fault nor his choice that his observations read like novels. But Freud confessed that neither his extensive neuro-anatomical knowledge nor the neuro-electrical experiences, which were the only therapeutic agents of his time, taught him the structure and cure of neurosis. It is assuredly one of the most powerful arguments. However, Pinel could hardly have remained faithful to such an argument; he confessed repeatedly that natural history served him as a model for the history of mental alienation. Observation and description are indeed the constituent elements of both histories. But the danger of venturing into and losing his way in a terrain foreign to science is surely present in the mind of an author who announces his own program in the following words:

> It is by no means a satire that I am undertaking; it is the history of a real disease that I intend to describe: all that is popularly understood by *delirium, extravagance, confusion, madness* must be foreign to me, as well as all metaphysical discussion, all hypothesis concerning the nature of intellectual or affective functions, their genesis, their order, their reciprocal interrelation, their succession . . . (3, pp. 4-5).

Broussais, a contemporary of Pinel, creator of the "physiological doctrine" and author of the important work entitled *Examen des doctrines médicales et des systèmes de nosologie*, reproaches Pinel with the very thing that we consider his claim to philosophical glory: his definition of diseases as "abstractions." Thanks to the development of philosophical and medical thought since the time of Pinel, and in spite of the obstacles confronting all classification and making it always a precarious and vulnerable undertaking, we should not forget that disease, in so far as it is an organized whole synthesized from perceptible data, is a product of human *thought*. The physician, then, is caught in the dilemma of either concerning himself with the individual and writing a biography or constructing a nosology composed, in fact, of anonymous entities in which the individual no longer has a place and life is no longer at its height. The root of this dilemma is therefore a dialectic involving two apparently irreconcilable terms: the general and the individual. Now, I maintain that the *individual is no less an abstraction than the disease appearing in nosology as an ontological entity*. The individual is not a sense impression passively received; the individual is rather an articulated whole built up in the mind of the observer by repeated experiences. He is a complex of sensations organized in accordance with the laws of understanding. In fact, he emerges towards the end, not at the beginning, of an investigation in which we exercise very active thought. The result of this investigation is neither definitive nor irrevocable, because our experience is never definitive.

In short, the individual is merely a unit composed of natural, but very heterogeneous, phenomena. This unit is conceived as the product of a unifying or integrating agent to which no concrete existence can be granted, since unification and integration exist only in *action*. In the midst of a world of data, unrelated and therefore tending toward confusion, integration must be accomplished continuously; consequently, the integrating agent can never be conceived in static terms. In passing from the disease to the diseased individual, *we do not pass from an intellectual structure or an idea to life itself, but only from an anonymous, neutral concept to one more personal but still intellectual.* Thought of in this way, the passage from nosology to biography does not reflect a difference of principle; it is none the less passage whose importance we should not underestimate. Nosography and biography represent, therefore, two *methods* of thinking, each justified in itself, but each serving a particular purpose. There is only one way to avoid the dangers and the pitfalls inherent in these two conflicting methods: namely, to be a biographer and temporarily forget the disease when dealing with the patient, but to be a nosographer and temporarily forget the patient when dealing with the disease.

These two methods, nosography and biography, not only reveal the power of the human intelligence, they reveal also the limitations imposed upon reason in its attempt to grasp the essence of nature, which eludes us. Nature itself contains no factor compelling us to choose one method and reject the other. No objection can be raised against those who abstain from practicing nosography and insist, at any price, upon being biographers. But they will make no contribution to the doctrine of diseases. They will make no discoveries in experimental therapeutics, since in experimental method their interest and attention will be concentrated upon the general and common result of a great number of experiences. Conversely, those who abstain from the biographical approach to devote themselves entirely to nosography will never attain the complete analysis of an individual phenomenon. What finally determines the choice of the method to be adopted is the difference in aims and in the tasks we wish to accomplish, not the subject of study; this subject is nature, which we shall never completely fathom. We do, in fact, have one intention in subjecting an individual experience to complete analysis, another in subjecting a number of individual experiences to grouping.

These limitations imposed upon reason become evident as soon as we attempt to use one of the two methods to the exclusion of the other. The neglected principle then intrudes surreptitiously into our interpretation. So it is that, in pursuing our efforts at classification, in the final analysis we reach a point where it is necessary to admit individual variations, so-called atypical or abortive pictures: nosography has yielded to biography. Conversely, the author of the Hippocratic observations, interpreting an individualization so extreme as to defy diagnosis and classification, has recourse to the modifications sustained by the individual under the influence of age, the seasons, waters, places, and political circumstances: biography has yielded to nosography.

An Eminent Opponent (Broussais)

Pinel's nosology, and the institution of *classifications* in general, did not remain without contradiction. Broussais, the founder of a once popular so-called physiological doctrine, was a violent opponent of Pinel's Hippocratic view of the natural history of diseases and their determined course as they appear in classifications.

Broussais (1772-1838) constructed, on the concept of irritability, another system of medicine, i.e., his once very popular but also much debated "physiological doctrine" (6a). He attributed irritability to all living beings and to all tissues, whereas he limited sensibility (i.e. the faculty to sense the movements excited by a foreign agent) to those animals which are endowed with a central nervous system. He believed "organic," i.e. an unconscious sensibility, to be a useless abstraction. He could reach this conclusion by declaring the movement of the stimulated fiber to be the sole visible phenomenon (*"le seul phénomène apparent"*) and by declaring it impossible to isolate sensing from moving (*"il est impossible d'isoler le sentir du se mouvoir"*). He thereby simplified the definition of animal life established by Aristotle, who distinguished movement and sensation as criteria of animal life. Life, Broussais concluded is due to the continuous influence exerted by numerous excitatory causes. Some of them reach the brain from outer objects, while others reach the tissues from the brain. Still other stimulations result from the movement of the fluids and, finally, from the reciprocal influences of the organs acting upon each other, either by way of the nerves or the brain. A dynamic aspect of this now forgotten so-called physiological doctrine is to be seen in the actions at a distance or the "organic sympathies" implied in Broussais' concept of nervous function. Ironically, Broussais himself, in his effort to combat classifications, referred to Condillac and his analytical method on which precisely Pinel's nosology rests. Those who establish classifications, Broussais said, make a faulty decomposition of the sum total of the pathological disorders which they do not analyze; to analyze means indeed to observe the qualities of a given object in a successive order so as to give to them in the mind simultaneously the order in which they exist (Condillac). But it is above all Broussais' objection to the natural history of disease which deserves the attention of the historian, since it seems to be the first *systematic* objection ever raised to the Hippocratic tradition and the legacy of the father of medicine. It was, however, not the last time that the objection was raised. The conception of the natural history of disease, its determined course, and the purely *observational* thought which is at its roots were bound not only to challenge the sceptical minds of those who, like Broussais, doubted the very possibility of a living organism ever being divorced from the influence of its ever-changing or threatening surroundings; the idea was also bound to provoke those aggressive and optimistic minds, like Claude Bernard's (11), almost a century after Broussais, who had to discard purely observational medicine from their vision of an experimental medicine, the essence and blessings of which rested precisely on its active nature and conquering spirit as opposed to the contemplative spirit of Hippocratic or purely observational medicine which favored expectation, regimen, and prognosis but did not reach out as yet for change, intervention, generous medication, or active therapy.

Pinel as a Teacher

An indication of Pinel's principles of clinical teaching is to be found in a memoir submitted in 1792 to the Société Royale de Médecine in a competition to determine the best method of clinical teaching in the hospital.

Pinel states in principle that the art of healing can be taught only in the hospital. ". . . it is necessary," he says, "to select a small number of patients for the instruction of the students, assembling these patients in so-called clinical wards."

In the establishment of this clinical hospital, the greatest attention should be paid to nosological meteorology. He insists that topography should be the subject of a special study, for, he says:

> . . . An exact topography is singularly suitable for throwing light upon the particular characteristics and treatment of those diseases which are ordinarily prevalent in the clinical wards, since it indicates the production of the soil, the mode of living of the inhabitants, their more or less active and laborious life,

the food which they consume and everything which can have a marked influence upon the animal economy and affect its functions.

. . . the large hospital is needed for surgery, whereas for medicine the hospital of medium size, such as the Charité, may be sufficient.

The clinician must fulfill the double function of an exact and faithful observer and of a skilled professor who must teach the young students the art of observing; but with what wise deliberation he must proceed in going from one patient to another; and how often his zeal, I should even say his enthusiasm, for the art that he professes must cause him to prolong beyond the assigned period the time that he devotes to a certain patient. It is the same with the practice of medicine as with the other arts and sciences: one has already made great progress when one has learned to work hard and to judge oneself with the greatest strictness even while others are most indulgent in their judgment (23, pp. 86-88).

Pinel is of the opinion that patients should be classified according to age and sex, and that their number should not exceed 18 to 24.

And since he believes that "the management of patients should differ as little as possible from the way of living of private individuals," he insists that wards which may contain three or four beds be divided "into compartments by special partitions so that each bed may be isolated from the others and that the condition of each patient may not be aggravated either by the sight of other infirmities which might distress him, or by foul odors or exhalations, or by contagious miasmata."

For Pinel is concerned with avoiding the contagion so frequent and so deadly in the hospital environment.

Pinel as an Interviewer

In that chapter of his *Traité Médico-Philosophique* in which Pinel discusses the defects of memory and of the association of ideas (considered by Condillac the "principle of insanity and reason": *Cours d'Etudes*, V, I, XIII, Conclusion) in mental alienation (3, p. 90), he reports on the behavior of a notary who had lost his *speech*.

Pinel must have been familiar with the problems implied in the interview, its structure, and the art of conducting it. But we cannot arrive at a sound notion of Pinel as an interviewer unless we understand the principles of the therapeutic *interview* of aphasics; and the latter cannot be understood unless we understand the principles of *aphasia.*

In the final analysis it is *knowledge* that is tested in the interview of an aphasic, knowledge of signs and symbols, of meanings and intentions, of organized motor patterns, verbal and pantomimic. This knowledge is that of a living human being. Any attempt to isolate the knowledge from the individual who gained, retained, regained, reshaped, or lost it, is bound to mislead the interviewer. In making such an attempt, the interviewer, anxious and even able to discover missing stones in his mosaic vision of the patient, fails to reach the human soil from which knowledge springs, in which it remains embedded and from which it disappears. Under these circumstances, the interviewer suffers from the self-inflicted inability to trace knowledge to its *biographic sources, to its original significance and to its metamorphosis in the march of time and events.*

The biographic sources of Pinel's diagnostic, prognostic, and therapeutical reasonings were stressed by me in my first publication on the subject (1951), when I declared Pinel's approach to the mentally ill to be a logical result of his *Hippocratic* view of disease as a historical chapter in an individual's life (46).

But can one still reach an authentic picture of a person's knowledge if one disregards the early and later individual versions and true content of that knowledge which, verbally speaking, seems to remain the same throughout life and whose changes remain hidden behind the façade of an identical term? Can one still reach a judgment as to an individual's knowledge without trying to decipher his *inner language,* the personal and often strange connotation which a term of speech may carry, the place left or denied to the term in the *system* of knowledge or experience of a mature or informed interviewee?

Here are the sources of the many neologisms which we encounter in so many philosophical systems and which we must tolerate in the language of the aphasic anxious to convey his knowledge to his listener in unmistakable and authentic terms. The investment of the interview with biographical implications becomes still greater when we allow these implications to extend to the interviewer himself. In any *examination* it is not only the examinee but also the examiner who is tested and who faces the stupendous task of formulating, in fairness and precision, questions the answers of which he might himself have been allowed to prepare in tranquillity and due time. It is understandable that an honest and mature interviewer might feel himself to be put to the test by the interviewee and thus occasionally be thrown into a state of defense and panic from which he may try to liberate himself by saving face or by retaliating, if not by neurotic mechanisms. In the light of the type of testing knowledge advocated here, it becomes imperative to include the whole biography of the patient in subjects discussed in the interview. In other words, the interviewer cannot forego the task of taking or retaking the clinical history, if only its essentials. There could be no better method of testing the interviewee's *terminology*, the ease with which some of the terms are used, the retardations suffered by others, the occasions when this happens, the vulnerable areas in the self-styled record of his own life, their effects on the fluency of his succeeding record, the genuine or spurious fatigue, or the wish to minimize or to break off the confessions transparent in his record.

Regardless of the site, the extent, or the nature of a cerebral lesion, there always remains the person, however inadequate, who suffers and rejoices; it is to him rather than to the structures that the physician and the psychologist turn in order to explore, to assist, to encourage, and to reeducate the patient. It is always for this reason that the voice of the patient, even in the presence of organic lesions, must be heard from the moment when the interviewer touches on those problems and subjects that have particular significance in the thought and instinctive life of the patient. Is it necessary to mention the trivial observation that the person who is being questioned will refuse to respond to an interviewer whom he suspects of lack of impartiality in questions relative to his life, the disease, or the commitment? Many times I have observed patients in an interview concealing resentment at what they had innocently interpreted as an affront to their dignity; the necessarily elementary and simple questions, "Where is your right arm?" or "Show me your tongue," made them suspicious. "I am not a fool," they might say. *Nothing human, great or small, true or false, needs necessarily to be lacking in a patient, whether or not he has sustained a brain lesion.* Such is the spirit which pervades Pinel's *Traité médico-philosophique sur l'aliénation mentale.* Such is also the spirit which characterized Pinel as an interviewer.

Pinel on Nominal Defects (Amnesic Aphasia)

"Q" A sort of alienation or delirium which follows an attack of apoplexy entails almost always a more or less noticeable diminution or loss of memory. This disorder may also be confined to the terms which serve to express ideas. A notary for whom my advice was sought had forgotten, after an attack of apoplexy, his own name, that of his wife, those of his children, and of his friends, although in other respects his tongue retained all its mobility; he no longer knew how to read or write, and nevertheless he seemed to remember objects which had previously made an impression upon his senses and which were associated with his profession as a notary. He was seen to point with his fingers to folders containing documents or contracts which others had been unable to find, and to indicate by other signs that he *preserved* the old chain of ideas (3, p. 90).

The case was listed by Pinel as a post-apoplectic state of "alienation or delirium" resulting in a memory defect. Thus, in his eyes, a purely *mechanical* factor, i.e., the lack of memory, seemed to be the sole responsible agent. But at this early stage of our knowledge of cerebral lesions, Pinel, with a flash of genius and inspired by his observational knowledge and newly gained interpretation of mental alienation rooted in human passions, soon turned to the *dynamics* in brain lesions, i.e., to the *selective* loss of memory: the preserved knowledge of the patient referred indeed to his profession, which apparently ranked higher in the hierarchy of his interests and ties than the names of his family and friends. But the whole case remained buried under the heading of "Memory Defects Encountered in Mental Alienation." In fact, Pinel could not have been expected to possess that knowledge and refined interpretation of speech defects resulting from brain lesions which was gained a century later. Not even the name of *aphasia* could have entered Pinel's mind and diagnostic reasoning. The patient obviously suffered from a *nominal defect*, defined in 1926 by Henry Head as "an inability to designate an object in words and to appreciate verbal meaning" (26).

It is true that,in all probability, the patient was not subject to the formal interview in which we test aphasics today. But the patient must have sensed the atmosphere and the frame of the nonverbal interview quasi "conducted" by those in search of the missing documents. Though they did not address the patient verbally, they stimulated his preserved knowledge and responses by their searching gestures and eloquent behavior. The patient's own gesture (he was seen to point with his fingers to folders containing documents or contracts which had not been located) can serve as a prelude to that chapter of the early history of aphasia which was written in the terms and concepts of what was then known and taught concerning the genesis and early history of *human language.*

The Language of Action According to Condillac

"Q" Gestures, facial expressions, inarticulate sounds: these were the first means that men possessed for communicating their thoughts to one another. The language formed by these signs is called *language* of action.

By gestures I mean the movements of the arm, of the head, of the whole body which withdraws from or approaches an object, and all the attitudes which we adopt according to the impressions which reach the mind.

Desire, refusal, disgust, aversion, etc., are expressed by movements of the arm, the head, and those of the whole body—movements more or less brisk according to the intensity with which we approach or withdraw from an object.

All the feelings of the soul may be expressed by bodily attitudes. They depict in a perceptible manner indifference, uncertainty, irresolution, attention, fear and desire commingled, the struggle among passions with first one and then another dominating, confidence and distrust, tranquil enjoyment and elated enjoyment, pleasure and pain, grief and joy, hope and despair, hate, love, anger.

But the elegance of this language is in the facial expressions, especially those of the eyes. These movements complete a picture which the bodily attitudes have merely sketched; and they

"Q' express the passions with all the modifications of which they are susceptible. . . .

This language is natural to all the individuals of the same species; nevertheless, all need to learn it. It is natural to them because, if a person who lacks the use of speech points to the object which he needs and expresses by other movements the desire which this object arouses in him, it is, as we have just noted, because of the structure of the organs. But if this person had not observed what his own body does in such a situation, he would not have been able to recognize a desire in another's movements. Hence he would not understand the meaning of movements made before him; he would not be capable of making similar ones intentionally in order to make himself understood. So this language is not so natural that one knows it without having learned it. The error into which you may fall in this matter proceeds from the fact that we are disposed to believe that we have learned only what we remember having studied. But to have learned is nothing more than to know at one time what one did not know previously. Indeed, whether, as a result of your structure, circumstances alone have taught you what you did not know, or whether you have taught yourself by deliberate study, it still is learning.

Since the language of action is a result of the structure of our organs, we did not choose its first signs. Nature gave them to us: but in giving them to us, she opened the way for us to devise some for ourselves. We could consequently express all our thoughts by gestures as we express them by words; and this language would be composed of natural signs and artificial signs. Note well that I say *artificial signs* and not *arbitrary signs*, for one must not confuse these two.

What, in fact, are arbitrary signs? Signs chosen unreasoningly and capriciously. Therefore, they would not be understood. On the contrary, artificial signs are signs whose choice is based upon reason: they must be devised with such art that comprehension of them has been prepared by signs already known (16, Vol. 1, pp. 428-431).

Epilogue

Pinel's Treatise on mental alienation (*Traité médico-philoso-phique sur l'aliénation mentale*, Paris, 1801) opened the early history of modern psychiatry. Pinel was deeply influenced by eighteenth century thought and, more particularly, by the teaching of Condillac —abbot, philosopher, educator, himself a pupil of John Locke and an apologist of a theory of experience resting primarily on the testimony of the senses, external and internal (reflection and its derivatives, i.e., discernment, comparison, judgment etc.). Pinel granted to the passions a decisive role in the genesis of mental alienation and in this respect proved to be a follower of Condillac rather than of Locke. Pinel designated his treatment as a moral one (*"traitement moral"*). But he was very far from judging his patients and their behavior ethically; he looked at their violent passions as at subjects of natural history. He repeatedly confessed his adherence to the principles of Hippocratic medicine and its observational spirit. He established faithful and repeated observation as the main criteria of experimental medicine, and he saw no rupture between ancient and modern medicine, no fundamental difference between observation and experimentation, the former merging into the latter and experimentation ultimately being nothing but observation made under special conditions and restrictions.

References

WORKS BY PINEL

1. Analyse. *Dictionnaire des sciences médicales*. Paris: Crapart et Pancoucke, 1812.
1a. *La médecine clinique rendue plus précise et plus exacte par l'application de l'analyse, ou recueil et résultat d'observations sur les maladies aïgues faites à la Salpétrière*. 2nd ed. Paris: J. A. Brosson, 1804.
2. *Nosographie philosophique ou la méthode de l'analyse appliquée à la médecine*. Vol. I. 4th ed. Paris: J. A. Brosson, 1798.
2a. *Nosographie philosophique ou la méthode de l'analyse appliquée à la médecine*. Vol. I, 4th ed. Paris: J. A. Brosson, 1810.
3. *Traité médico-philosophique sur l'aliénation mentale*. 2nd ed. Paris: J. A. Brosson, 1809.
4. *A Treatise on Insanity in Which Are Contained the Principles of a New and More Practical Nosology of Maniacal Disorders than Has Yet Been Offered to the Public*. Translated from the French by D. D. Davis, M.D. Printed by W. Todd for Cadell and Davies, Strand, London, 1806. (A facsimili reprint of this edition has been published by the Hafner Publishing Company, New York City, 1962, with an introduction by Dr. Paul F. Cranefield.)
5. Mémoire sur la manie périodique ou intermittente. *Mém. de la Soc. Méd. d'Emulat.* de Paris, Vol. I, 1797.
5a. Observations sur les aliénés et leur division en espèces distinctes. *Mém. de la Soc. Méd. d'Emulat.* de Paris, Vol. III, 1799.
5b. *Pinel Cross Reference:* Un mémoire inédit de Pinel sur l'enseignement clinique, by M. Genty. *Le Progrès Médical, Suppl.,* 1935 *(see also* ref. 23).

WORKS BY OTHERS

6. Ackerknecht, E. Biographical note by E. Ackerknecht: *Kurze Geschichte der Psychiatrie*. Stuttgart: Ferdinand Enke Verlag, 1957.
6a. Ackerknecht, E. Broussais, or a forgotten medical revolution. *Bull. Hist. Med.,* 27: 320-343, 1963.
7. Aurelanius, Caelius. *On Acute Diseases and on Chronic Diseases*. Edited and translated by I. E. Drabkin. Chicago: The University of Chicago Press, 1950.
8. Bacon. *The Works of Francis Bacon with a Life of the Author,* by Basil Montagu. Philadelphia: 1889.
9. Baruk, H. La morale en psychologie et en psychopathologie. *Revue Philosophique, CLIII,* 1963.
10. Baruk, H. La psychiatrie et les sciences de l'homme. *Note e Riviste di Psichiatria*. Vol. 4, Oct.-Dec., 1956.

11. Bernard, C. *Principes de médecine expérimentale*. Paris: Presses Universitaires de France, 1947.

12. Bertocci, A. Lecture Notes on Montaigne's *Essays*. Unpublished manuscript. Cambridge, Harvard University: 1956.

13. Cabanis, P. J. G. *Rapports du physique et du moral*. Corpus Général des Philosophes Français. Part I, Vol. XLIV. Paris: Presses Universitaires de France, 1956.

14. Calmeil, J. B. *De la folie considérée sous le point de vue pathologique, philosophique, historique et judiciaire*. Paris: J. B. Baillière, 1845.

15. Carlson, E. T., and Norman, D. The psychotherapy that was moral treatment. *The Amer. J. of Psychiat.*, *117*:519-524, 1960.

16. Condillac. *Oeuvres philosophiques de Condillac*. Paris: Presses Universitaires de France, 1947.

17. Cuvier, G. *Rapport historique sur le progrès des sciences naturelles depuis 1789, et sur leur état actuel*. Paris: de L'Imprimerie Impériale, 1810.

18. Deichgräber, K. *Die griechische Empirikerschule*. Berlin, Zürich: Weidmannsche Verlags-Buchhandlung, 1905.

19. Descartes, R. *Descartes' Philosophical Writings*. Translated and selected by Norman Kemp Smith. London: MacMillan & Company, Ltd., 1952.

20. Descartes, R. *Discours de la méthode*, Commentary by Etienne Gilson. Paris: Librairie Philosophique J. Vrin, 1962.

21. Descartes, R. *Les Passions de l'âme*. Paris: Bibliothèque de la Pléiade. Paris: Gallimard, 1952.

21a. *Dictionnaire de l'Académie Française*. 4th ed. Paris, 1762.

21b. *L'Encyclopédie ou Dictionnaire Raisonné des Sciences, des Arts et des Métiers*, edited by Diderot and d'Alembert, 1777.

21c. *L'Encyclopédie et le Progrès des Sciences et des Techniques*. Paris: Presses Universitaires de France, 1952.

22. Ferriar, John (Physiciun to the Manchester Infirmari). *Medical Histories and Reflexions*. 1795.

23. Genty, M. Un mémoire inédit de Pinel sur l'enseignement clinique. *Le Progrès Médical. Suppl.*, 1935.

23a. Gilson, E. Descartes' *Discours de la méthode*, Commentary by Etienne Gilson. Paris: Librairie Philosophique J. Vrin, 1962.

24. Haslam, John. *Observations on Insanity, with Practical Remarks on the Disease and an Account of the Morbid Appearances on Dissection*. London: 1794, P. XLV.

25. Hazard, P. *La pensée européenne au XVIIIième siècle de Montesquieu à Lessing*. Vol. 1. Paris: Boivin et Cie., 1946.

26. Head, H. *Aphasia and Kindred Disorders of Speech*. Cambridge: University Press, 1926.

27. Kraft, I. Edouard Seguin and the 19th century moral treatment of idiots. *Bull. Hist. Med.*, *35*:393-418, 1961.

28. Lechler, W. H. *Philippe Pinel, seine Familie, seine Jugend und Studienjahre, 1745-1778*. Munich: 1959.

29. Leroy, A. L. *Locke, sa vie, son oeuvre, avec un exposé de sa philosophie.* Paris: Presses Universitaires de France, 1964.

30. Lhermitte, J. *Vrais et faux possédés.* Paris: Librairie Arthème Fayard, 1956.

31. Locke, J. *An Essay Concerning Human Understanding.*

32. Montaigne. *Essays.* Translated by Charles Cotton; W. Carew Hazlitt (Ed.). Encyclopedia Britannica. Vol. 2, 1955.

33. Oesterreich, T. K. *Possession Demoniacal and Other Among Primitive Races, in Antiquity, the Middle Ages, and Modern Times.* New Hyde Park, New York: University Books, 1966.

34. Pariset, E. Eloge de Pinel. *Mémoires de l'Académie de Médecine.* Vol. I. Paris: 1828.

35. Plato. *Plato's Theory of Knowledge. The Theaetetus and the Sophist of Plato.* Translated by Francis MacDonald Cornford. London: Routledge and Kegan Paul, Ltd., 1949.

35a. Prichard, J. C. A Treatise on Insanity and Other Disorders Affecting the Mind, 1835, p. 169. In: *The Historical Development of British Psychiatry.* Vol. I, 18th and 19th Centuries by Denis Leigh. New York, Oxford, London, Paris: Pergamon Press, 1961.

36. Riese, W. Descartes as a psychotherapist. The uses of rational philosophy in the treatment of discomfort and disease; its limitations. *Med. Hist.,* X: 237-244, 1966.

37. Riese, W. Descartes' Ideas of Brain Function. Lecture delivered on July 15, 1957, in London to the Anglo-American Symposium on the History and Philosophy of Knowledge of the Brain and its Functions. In *The History and Philosophy of Knowledge of the Brain and Its Functions,* F. N. L. Poynter (Ed.). Oxford: Blackwell Scientific Publications, 1958. Pp. 115-134.

38. Riese, W. History and principles of classification of nervous diseases. *Bull. Hist. Med., 18*:465-512, 1945.

39. Riese, W. The impact of 19th century thought on psychiatry. *Internat. Record of Med., 173*:7-19, 1960.

40. Riese, W. Kurt Goldstein — the man and his work. In: *The Reach of Mind: Essays in Memory of Kurt Goldstein.* Marianne L. Simmel (Ed.) New York: Springer Publishing Company, Inc., 1968.

41. Riese, W. Neuropsychologic phase in the history of psychiatric thought. In: *Historic Derivations of Modern Psychiatry.* Iago Galdston, M.D. (Ed.). New York: McGraw-Hill Book Co., 1967.

42. Riese, W. The 150th anniversary of S. T. Soemmerring's "Organ of the Soul." *Bull. Hist. Med., 20*:310-321, 1946.

43. Riese, W. On thought in existentialism. *J. of Existentialism, 6*:89-97, 1965.

44. Riese, W. An outline of a history of ideas in psychotherapy. *Bull. Hist. Med., 25*:442-456, 1951.

45. Riese, W. La pensée causale en médecine. Paris: Presses Universitaires de France, 1950.

46. Riese, W. Philippe Pinel (1745-1826). His views on human nature and disease, his medical thought. *J. Nerv. and Ment. Dis., 114*:313-323, 1951.

47. Riese, W. Phyloanalysis (Burrow), its historical and philosophical implications. *Supp. ad Acta Psychotherapeutica and Psychosomatica, 11*:5-36, 1963.

48. Riese, W. The pre-Freudian origins of psychoanalysis. In: *Science and Psychoanalysis.* Vol. I, Integrative Studies, Jules H. Masserman (Ed.). New York: Grune & Stratton, Inc., 1958, Pp. 29-72.

49. Riese, W. The principle of compensation of nervous function. *J. Nerv. and Ment. Dis., 100*:263-274, 1944.

50. Riese, W. The principle of diaschisis, its history, its nature, and its general significance. *International Record of Medicine, 171*:73-82, 1958.

51. Riese, W. The principle of evolution of nervous function. *J. Nerv. and Ment. Dis., 98*:255-266, 1943.

52. Riese, W. Le raisonnement expérimental dans l'oeuvre de Pinel. *L'Evolution Psychiatrique, 31*:407-413, 1966.

53. Riese, W. The sources of Pinel's view on mental alienation. *Archivos de Neurobiologia, XXVIII,* (4), 753-771, 1965.

54. Riese, W. La théorie des passions à la lumière de la pensée médicale du XVIIe siècle. Suppl. to *Confinia Psychiat. Vol. 8.* Basle-New York: S. Karger, 1965.

55. Riese, W., and Gooddy, W. An original clinical record of Hughlings Jackson with an interpretation. *Bull. Hist. Med., 29*:230-238, 1955.

56. Riese, W., and Harkins, P. W. *Galen on the Passions and Errors of the Soul.* Translation from the Greek by Dr. P. W. Harkins. Introduction and interpretation by W. Riese. Columbus: Ohio State University Press, 1963.

57. Rosen, G. The philosophy of ideology and the emergence of modern medicine in France. *Bull. Hist. Med., 20*:328-339, 1946.

58. Rousseau, J. J. *A Discourse on the Origin of Inequality.* Translated with an introduction by G. D. H. Cole. New York: E. P. Dutton & Sons, Inc., 1947.

59. Rousseau, J. J. *A Discourse on the Origin of Inequality.* Translated by G. D. H. Cole. (Great Books) Chicago, London, Toronto: Encyclopedia Britannica, 1952.

60. Rousseau, J. J. *Oeuvres de J. J. Rousseau.* Paris: A. Bélin, 1817.

61. Saussure, R. de. *Ciba Symposia, 11,* (5) 1950.

62. Semelaigne, R. *Aliénistes et philanthropes. Les Pinel et les Tuke.* Paris: G. Steinheil, Edit., 1912.

63. Seneca. On anger (*De ira*).

64. Seneca. On the happy life (*De vita beata*).

65. Tracy, D. de. *Élements d'idéologie,* Part I, 3rd ed. Mme. Ve. Courcier, 1817.

66. Villey, P. *Essays of Michel de Montaigne.* Paris: Presses Universitaires de France, 1965.

67. Whitwell, J. R. *Historical Notes on Psychiatry.* London: H. K. Lewis and Co., Ltd., 1936.

Index